SMOKE SCREEN: TOBACCO AND THE PUBLIC WELFARE

SMOKE SCREEN: TOBACCO AND THE PUBLIC WELFARE

Maurine B. Neuberger

Prentice-Hall, Inc., Englewood Cliffs, N. J.

Smoke Screen: Tobacco and the Public Welfare
by Maurine B. Neuberger.

© 1963 by Prentice-Hall, Inc., Englewood Cliffs, N. J.

Library of Congress Catalog Card Number: 63-19623

Printed in the United States of America

T 81485

To the physicians and scientists whose labors unmasked the role of smoking in disease, this book is dedicated.

Acknowledgments

Because I first became involved with the public health aspects of smoking as a legislator—not an author—my Senate office soon became a virtual clearinghouse for the comments, papers and arguments of literally hundreds of physicians, scientists and laymen concerned about smoking. A perceptive insight here, a novel suggestion there, a clipping, a complaint— each contributed in some indefinable measure to the background, views and comments now developed in this book. I do not know how to acknowledge these contributions individually, but I would be neglectful if I failed to mention them.

This book grew out of my personal involvement in the subject, but some very special acknowledgments are important:

My personal physician, Dr. Morton Goodman, who over the years never said, "Stop smoking," but carefully subjected me to the overwhelming evidence that there was a very real cause-and-effect relationship between cigarette smoking and health.

My husband, Dick, who never smoked himself, never nagged at me, but who was so proud and pleased when I finally quit.

Special mention goes to Alexander R. Beard, a devoted correspondent, who kept me supplied with helpful newspaper clippings on the subject of smoking.

I have been skillfully guided through the medical and scientific evidence by Dr. Michael Shimkin and Dr. Daniel Horn. Each of them scrutinized the manuscript for errors that might not have been evident to a layman. Neither of them can be shouldered with responsibility for those errors which undoubtedly remain.

Stanley Cohen, Washington editor of *Advertising Age*, whose understanding of the special world of cigarette advertising is widely recognized, has been a consultant on advertising fact and folklore.

Members of my own staff have contributed by research, weekend and late-night typing, even foregoing vacation time. The mainstay of this group was my Legislative Assistant, Mike Pertschuk.

In developing my legislative position on smoking, I was also fortunate to be able to draw upon the resourceful research talents of Lila Nolan and Jane Malone of the Library of Congress.

The staff and officers of the Tobacco Institute were helpful in supplying material and at all times were friendly and courteous, despite my disaffection with their own industry. I am also grateful to the P. Lorillard Company for providing an enlightening tour of its plant and research facilities.

Contents

Introduction

Shortly after I had taken the floor of the Senate to plead for the enactment of rational public health measures to curb what a leading scientist had called the "cigarette epidemic," I found that a curious change took place in my life. For weeks after I had spoken, friends, colleagues, and even near-strangers whom I met would spontaneously launch into grim accounts of their own combat with the smoking habit. I became, quite against my will, confidante, counselor, and confessor to many in the smoking populace of the nation's capital. I began to suspect that I would end my days in Washington a social pariah, especially when the wife of a Cabinet member confided to me that my presence at a party was good for her husband—he always smoked considerably less when I was around!

For every tale of triumph over tobacco, I have heard twenty of the "I know I should quit, but . . ." variety. But nothing so disarmed me as the wry note I received from a dear friend and Senate colleague, the day after I had cornered him and de-

tailed the indictment against smoking in as terrifying terms as
I could muster:

> As I told you riding over to the Capitol yesterday, it was my
> firm intention to make this a denunciatory letter following
> receipt of your invitation to join you in sponsoring your
> resolution to create a Commission on Tobacco and Health.
> Between coughs, I now announce that although I cannot go
> so far as to join with you in sponsorship (yet, at any rate),
> I have been thinking during the hours since we talked almost
> constantly of your having told me of having seen in a color
> film the lungs of the heavy smoker. Indeed, the whole epi-
> sode made me so nervous that I have been smoking like
> fury ever since.

He had in good humor laid bare one of the disturbing
paradoxes that continues to characterize the smoking problem in this country. Though there remain many smokers—and
children eager to become smokers—who are still misled or
lulled by the distortions and semantic quibbles of tobacco
industry spokesmen, vast numbers of others are neither confused nor misled but perversely continue "smoking like fury."

Shortly after the publication in the spring of 1962 of the
Royal College of Physicians' exhaustive documentation of the
case against smoking, a journalist writing in the noted British
medical journal, *The Lancet*, had this to say:

> Future historians will have views on our failure to find even
> a partial solution to the problem of smoking during the first
> ten years after its dangers were revealed. The enormous and
> increasing number of deaths from smoker's cancer may go
> down in history as a strong indictment of our political and
> economic ways of life.

Yet, *which* segments of our society and *which* institutions
will these "future historians" indict? The tobacco industry,
for its callous and myopic pursuit of its own self-interest? The

government, for its timidity and inertia in failing to formulate a positive program of prophylaxis? The medical profession, for abdicating its role of leader in this crucial area of public health? Or is the individual—smoker and nonsmoker alike—incriminated by his failure to accept responsibility for his own and his society's well-being? I am convinced that no indictment would be sufficient if it failed to name each of these parties jointly responsible for the "cigarette epidemic."

I have undertaken to write this book because I believe that the moral and intellectual poverty that has characterized our approach to the smoking problem must no longer be shrouded by the press-agentry of the tobacco industry, nor the fancy bureaucratic footwork of government agencies charged with responsibility for guarding the nation's health.

Yet, polemics alone cannot retard the incidence of death and debilitation from smoking. As I have learned more of the hazards of smoking, so I have become sensitive to the complex barriers—social and psychological, political and economic—which frustrate easy solutions to the smoking problem. And as Rachel Carson has shown us in *Silent Spring*, the stronger the vested interest threatened, the more imposing the barriers.

There is no simple remedy. Prohibition is neither feasible nor compatible with our traditional freedom of choice. We have amply demonstrated that we are not a nation of prohibitionists. Nevertheless, there are practical and judicious measures which can effectively be employed to brake the rising toll of smokers. It is my purpose and hope in this book to enlist the support of my readers in the task of implementing such measures.

Finally, although I cannot pretend to be an expert in the sciences of chemistry, pharmacology, epidemiology (the study of the factors which determine the frequency and distribution of a disease or a condition in a population), and so forth, no book on smoking would be complete without at least a rudimentary tour through the vast storehouse of medical evidence incriminating smoking as a major cause of disease. Nor should any book on smoking avoid exposing the claims of the tobacco apologists. I have therefore attempted at least to touch upon the high spots in the quest for knowledge of the effects of smoking, as well as the low spots in the tobacco industry's pseudoscientific guerrilla warfare.

1

"They're So Mild!"

Mice are unenthusiastic smokers. For one thing, a mouse has to inhale through his nose since, unlike a human, he cannot breathe through his mouth. If he does succeed in sniffing in quantities of smoke in the same concentrations as inhaled by human smokers, he is likely to go into convulsions and expire on the spot. But let us assume that we are able over a period of several years to breed a generation of mice foolhardy enough to smoke regularly, and hardy enough to survive. Then assume that we spent the next several years comparing their subsequent health histories with those of a control group of abstinent mice; if we found that our smoking mice alone succumbed to lung cancer and premature heart failure, the tobacco industry presumably would hail our experiment as proof positive of the hazards of smoking. Meanwhile, of course, hundreds of thousands of Americans would have become lung-cancer victims and millions would have suffered premature heart fatalities that otherwise might have been prevented. We might have satisfied at last, however, the tobacco industry's hunger for "pure clinical" evidence of the hazards of smoking.

1

Or would we? We could say with absolute certainty *only* that the mice we had trained to smoke ought to give up the habit. After all, the perfect laboratory animal for proving effects upon man is not the mouse but man. In order to construct the most nearly ideal experiment for gauging the effects of smoking upon human health, the investigator should select a random group of human beings, teach them to smoke, and record their subsequent deterioration, meanwhile comparing their health histories with those of a comparably selected group of nonsmokers.

This is precisely the experiment performed through the 1950's by Drs. E. Cuyler Hammond and Daniel Horn of the American Cancer Society, except that fortunately for both their consciences and convenience there already existed at large in our population 70,000,000 people who voluntarily and regularly smoked. With the help of 22,000 trained American Cancer Society volunteers, Hammond and Horn enrolled 187,783 men between the ages of 50 and 69 in a massive study of the relationship between smoking and health. The smoking or nonsmoking habits of each man were precisely noted. Then Hammond and Horn sat back and waited.

On October 31, 1953, they took a preliminary look at the comparative death rates of smokers and nonsmokers. That look was so startling that Dr. Horn, previously a moderately heavy smoker, never smoked cigarettes again.

By October 31, 1955, the evidence had become overwhelming. Of 11,870 men in the study group who had died, 7,316 were smokers. If the death rate of the smokers had been comparable to the death rate of the nonsmokers, only 4,651 would have died. The doctors therefore concluded that the deaths of 2,265 smokers had to be considered as "excess deaths" and related to smoking. Coronary artery disease claimed more than half these excess deaths. Lung cancer took 14 per cent, as much as all other cancers. Also prominent among the causes of "excess deaths" were cancer of the larynx and the esophagus, gastric ulcers, pneumonia, and influenza.

The death rate of regular cigarette smokers generally was 68 per cent higher than that of nonsmokers; that of smokers of two or more packs a day was 123 per cent higher. Cigar smokers had only a 22 per cent higher death rate, while the pipe smokers escaped relatively unscathed with a death rate only 12 per cent in excess of nonsmokers.

A very important finding was that ex-smokers had significantly lower death rates than those who continued to smoke regularly. The longer the ex-smoker had abstained, the more his death rate resembled that of the nonsmoker.

Though in absolute numbers heart disease claimed the most victims among the smokers, the ratio of smoker lung-cancer fatalities to nonsmoker fatalities was the most startling statistic of all. Lung-cancer fatalities were ten times as frequent in smokers as in nonsmokers. Even more startling, the chances of the heavy smoker dying of lung cancer was found to be *64 times that of the nonsmoker.*

Of the total of 127 deaths from cancer of the mouth, tongue, lip, larynx, pharynx, and esophagus, only four occurred in men who never smoked. Incidentally, it was here that the pipe and cigar smokers came into their own statistically, for their death rates from these diseases were far higher than those of the nonsmokers.

(Most cigarette smokers, of course, inhale. As one of the less ingenuous Lucky Strike ads put it: "Seven out of ten inhale knowingly—the other three do so unknowingly!" The great initial succes of the milder Virginia tobaccos in cigarettes can be traced, in large part, to the reduced alkalinity of smoke from Virginia leaf—a quality which enabled the smoker to inhale freely without coughing. Pipe and cigar smoke, on the other hand, is far more alkaline, and, as many men partial to those devices will tell you, it takes a rare and hardy creature to inhale either cigar or pipe smoke. Though pipe and cigar tobaccos generally produce more tar and nico-

tine, these are not destined to be sucked into the linings of
the lung.)

The Hammond and Horn study was certainly a landmark
in the history of knowledge about smoking. But their findings have been repeated and corroborated many times over.
The Royal College of Physicians reviewed 23 retrospective
studies in nine countries and four follow-up studies in three
countries. Among the latter were the Doll-Hill study of more
than 40,000 British physicians over the age of 35 and the Dorn
study of 249,000 United States veterans. In each case the Hammond and Horn findings were substantially duplicated.

Today Dr. Hammond is engaged in a mammoth study of
1,079,000 men and women over the age of 30. He has attempted to obtain as exhaustive and probing information
about his subjects as possible. To date, returns from this study
in no way contradict the earlier findings. Moreover, the new
study apparently provides evidence, previously lacking, of the
importance of inhaling. Upon the basis of preliminary data,
Dr. Hammond reported that "the degree of inhalation is as
important, and perhaps more important, than the amount of
smoking." Dr. Hammond has also alluded to evidence that
among subjects who had begun smoking during their teen-age
years the death rate by ages 30-35 is many times that of their
nonsmoking classmates.

As each successive population study appears to reinforce
the link between smoking and disease on a scale more grand,
more precise, and more exhaustive than the last, the tobacco
industry spokesmen rise like persistent spectres to be counted
with the "know-nothings." "Not proven," states the Tobacco
Institute (the industry's public relations organ). "Not
proven," states Dr. Clarence Cook Little, Chairman of the
Scientific Advisory Board of the Tobacco Industry Research
Committee. "Not proven," states the American Tobacco
Company, Reynolds, Philip Morris, *et al.* And once again
the claim, "merely statistical," is launched around the conti-

nent to make certain that no American makes the tragic error of believing the evidence and, God forbid, giving up smoking.

To the appalling discovery that women who had taken thalidomide during pregnancy were giving birth to deformed babies, the response of American Public Health officials was swift and sure. Thalidomide was swept off the market, and its use, even on an experimental basis, was totally proscribed. The evidence that thalidomide caused these birth defects was "merely statistical"; that is, the use of thalidomide and the birth of deformed babies tended to coincide. Yet we heard no anguished appeals from the manufacturer of thalidomide that the Government postpone action until laboratory scientists were able to prove that thalidomide administered to pregnant mice produced deformed baby mice. Nevertheless, the tobacco industry insists that statistical evidence is inherently defective. Dr. David Rutstein, head of the Department of Preventive Medicine at Harvard Medical School, took the measure of this contention in a telling open letter to Dr. Little published in the *Atlantic Monthly:*

Do not statistical principles come into play whenever anything is counted in any scientific study, whether performed in the laboratory or in the field? Statistics are, after all, the rules by which things are counted, and it is impossible to do any experiment without counting up the results.

. . . When you question the eighteen studies [note: now 23] which show a relationship between cigarette smoking and lung cancer as being only "statistical," I think what you really mean is that these studies are not as well controlled as laboratory experiments. If we think about it, we realize that even in laboratory experiments, no matter how performed, the results are really nothing more than a statistical association between two events. The laboratory result becomes more valid if one can perform a series of experiments in sequence because one can frequently rule out factors which may interfere with its interpretation.

On the other hand, in the study of epidemics of disease as they occur in a population, one can only observe what actually happens. This is as true for epidemics of influenza as it is for the present epidemic of lung cancer. This limitation does not deny the validity of the epidemiologic observation; it merely demands more care in interpretation. It requires analysis of the plan and results of each study and a comparison of the data of many studies planned along different lines. In the case of cigarette smoking and lung cancer, one may get some reassurance from the unanimity of results from the many different approaches that were used in the eighteen studies. It is unlikely that all would have been affected in exactly the same way by extraneous factors.

The tobacco industry's contempt for statistical evidence is not shared, incidentally, by the insurance industry (hardly noted for reckless risk-taking). Several insurance firms are now offering a substantial discount on life insurance to applicants who have not smoked for 24 months prior to their application and who are willing to forswear smoking for the foreseeable future.

Actually, even the tobacco industry succumbs on occasion to the lure of a relevant statistic. As Lord Cohen drily observed in the British House of Lords debate on smoking:

> . . . I have little doubt that the noble Lord's Tobacco Manufacturing Standing Committee and other bodies have not increased the expenditure in the last five years on tobacco advertisements by nearly four times without having had some statistical evidence to support the expenditure of that sum of money.

Tobacco apologists, though continuing to frown at the mention of statistical evidence, have by and large abandoned the pretense of earlier years that smokers are as equally hearty and healthy a lot as nonsmokers. Even they now generally concede that smokers fill the ranks of those most often felled by lung disease, coronaries, and so on.

But, says a physician in a paper often quoted by the Tobacco Institute: ". . . are we mistaking a concomitant for a cause? I am positive we are. . . ." This is to argue that certain unfortunate members of society are fated by heredity (1) to smoke and (2) to succumb prematurely to heart failure, lung cancer, and so forth, and that even if you could inhibit their genetic predisposition to smoke you would not reduce their risk of premature death. Plainly, since their fate is conveniently predetermined, it would be fruitless for them to give up smoking.

There are fatal flaws in any theory which attempts to explain the smokers' morbidity and mortality rate purely in terms of hereditary or genetic factors. To be consistent, for example, the Institute would have to add that those whose heredity doomed them to smoke and to an early eclipse must also be, by heredity, predisposed against membership in the Seventh Day Adventist Church, since a survey of Seventh Day Adventists, militant nonsmokers, disclosed a virtual absence of lung cancer. Indeed, in a group of Seventh Day Adventist patients in a Los Angeles hospital only two were found to have succumbed to lung cancer—two converts, who previously had smoked from childhood to near middle age.

Moreover, to account for smokers who have in fact proved themselves capable of giving up smoking and whose death rate has subsequently dropped sharply, it must follow that he who inherits the ability to give up smoking does not inherit the predisposition to premature death.

Next, our hereditary smoker-lung cancer victim-non-Seventh Day Adventist must also inherit ignorance, since various studies have shown that those who are aware of the dangers of smoking are less likely to smoke (and therefore to succumb to smoking-connected ailments) than their uninformed brethren.

And since the population studies demonstrated that the heavier the smoking habit, the greater the risk of disease, the heredity theory must also be expanded to postulate that those who inherit the urge to smoke a half-pack a day, inherit a correspondingly lower predisposition to disease than those who inherit the urge to smoke more than two packs a day.

It is of course possible that genetic factors do play a role in determining which smokers will succumb to lung cancer or heart disease (though it is unlikely that genetic good fortune can shield any smoker from chronic lung disease). It is equally clear that such genetic factors, whatever they may be, are inoperative among nonsmokers.

The frantic scramble to discredit population studies and unearth some fanciful cause, other than the inhalation of cigarette smoke, for the relationship between smoking and disease might be justified if we had no clinical or laboratory evidence that cigarette smoke is a hazardous substance. But do not suppose that the laboratory scientists were idle while others were out in the world counting heads and bodies. For more than a half-century we have been compiling dramatic clinical evidence of the disastrous effects of cigarette smoke upon human tissues and systems.

Smoke, the by-product of combustion, has long fascinated the medical researcher. Chemists early discovered that any organic matter subjected to extreme heat (and a hearty drag on a cigarette can produce temperatures in excess of 700 degrees Centigrade—though the smoke cools to room temperature before entering the mouth) produces a fascinating assortment of complex gases and chemical compounds. The cancer-causing (carcinogenic) properties of smoke had first been suspected by Sir Percival Pott, in 1775, who speculated that the tragic frequency of cancer of the scrotum among chimney sweeps appeared to be caused by their excessive contact with soot.

In 1925 the British chemist Sir Ernest L. Kennaway put match to virtually every organic substance he could lay his hands on—petroleum, coal, skin, hair, yeast, cholesterol—and in each case was able to produce cancerous tumors on the skins of laboratory animals by painting the condensed smoke "tar" upon their skins.

Tar may be a simple-sounding word, but the term "tobacco tar" is the chemists' shorthand for the composite of approximately 2,000 distinct chemical compounds isolated or remaining to be isolated from condensed tobacco smoke. And at least sixteen of these compounds, with such strange and exotic-sounding names as diketene and vinylcyclohexene hydroperoxide, have been found to be carcinogenic when administered to laboratory animals.

Ironically, one of the most significant of these carcinogens, 3,4-benzpyrene, was isolated in tobacco smoke by Dr. Samuel Z. Cardon while he was engaged in research financed in part by a tobacco company. (Shortly after his discovery tobacco company funds abruptly ran dry.)

Perhaps as significant as the carcinogens in the tobacco smoke are the cocarcinogens, which cannot produce cancer alone but, in conjunction with carcinogens, appear to stimulate greatly the growth of cancerous tumors. Two groups of chemical compounds present in tobacco smoke—phenols and fatty acids—have exhibited significant cocarcinogenic effects upon laboratory animals.

At this moment, the member of the panel representing the tobacco industry viewpoint jumps up, pounds the podium, and exclaims that cancer in mice is not cancer in human beings. "All this proves is that mice shouldn't go around painting their skins with tobacco tars. It certainly doesn't prove that smoke has any carcinogenic effect upon human tissue."

Yet the type of cancer (epidermoid carcinoma) produced on the skin of laboratory animals by the application of tobacco tars is identical to that cancer found on the lips, tongues, and mucous membranes of the mouth linings of smokers only. These, of course, are the tissues which, like the skin of the laboratory animals, come into direct contact with tobacco smoke as it is inhaled in quantities comparable to those applied to the laboratory animals.

Moreover, recent laboratory studies by Dr. Hammond and his associates have provided new and compelling insights into the mechanism by which cigarette smoke causes both lung cancer and premature heart disease.

Earlier studies had shown that inhaled cigarette smoke paralyzes the short, hairlike cilia whose constant whiplike motion propelling a layer of mucus as if it were on a conveyor belt, prevents irritants from settling in the bronchial tubes. Researchers had speculated that, unprotected by the action of the cilia, the bronchial tube linings would be subjected to a rain of carcinogens, cocarcinogens, and other irritants in the tobacco smoke.

Dr. Hammond, with Drs. Oscar Auerbach, Purdy Stout and others performed microscopic examinations of lung tissues taken from more than 1,000 patients who had died from a great variety of causes. They were able to compare the cancerous lung tissue of lung-cancer victims with the noncancerous lung tissue of both smokers and nonsmokers. In all of the smokers—and in none of the nonsmokers—they found the cilia destroyed. And where the cilia had been destroyed, they found cancer cells. These cancer cells, found rarely in the tissues of nonsmokers, occurred with great frequency in regular smokers. In heavy smokers the cancer cells were found in profusion, frequently combined to form precancerous lesions.

In studying the smokers' lung tissues, Auerbach and the others also discovered changes which shed light upon the smokers' susceptibility to heart disease. They found widespread destruction of the tiny air sacs, called alveoli, of the lung, as well as a narrowing of the small arterial blood vessels in the lungs. Since the heart must pump blood to the lungs to obtain oxygen from the alveoli, the destruction of alveoli and the narrowing of the blood vessels combine not only to force the heart to exert greater pressure, but also (simultaneously) to diminish the heart muscle's vital oxygen supply. Moreover, the remaining alveoli may hold, instead of oxygen, carbon monoxide inhaled with the cigarette smoke, thus further depleting the heart's oxygen supply.

Nor is the dismal picture complete without that traditional villain, nicotine. If you don't believe tobacco is truly lethal, ask a tobacco farmer. He uses nicotine (distilled from tobacco) in the pesticides he employs to protect his tobacco crop. And nicotine is the very model of an effective pesticide, penetrating the vital organs of the insect's body and producing, in the words of a pesticide manual, "stupefaction," "paralysis of the hind legs," "staggering gait," and "violent convulsions."

It was early discovered that nicotine, absorbed into the body in cigarette smoke, causes a narrowing or constriction of the peripheral arteries, adding to the load on an already strained and overburdened heart.

Arteriosclerosis, the building up of fatty deposits in the arteries with a consequent narrowing of the arterial passages, is known to be present in varying degree in the great majority of adult American males. Where the involuntary condition of arteriosclerosis coincides with the voluntary condition of smoking, it is no great surprise that heart failure is the frequent result.

"All right, then," says the tobacco man, "what about air pollution? What makes you think that it's cigarette smoke that scourges our lungs rather than the dust and fumes of our roads and cities?" There is, of course, excellent evidence that air pollution from the burning of such organic fuels as coal and oil is a contributing cause of the diseases associated with smoking. Why shouldn't it be? As we have seen, the combustion of almost any organic matter produces carcinogenic agents. As a polluter, the smoker is a blood brother of the fall leaf-burner. Dr. Michael B. Shimkin, Associate Director for Field Studies of the National Cancer Institute and a leading authority on smoking and disease, views the cigarette smoker drolly as a "do-it-yourselfer" who insists upon manufacturing his own personal smog cloud.

As to the relative importance of smoking and air pollution, the Hammond-Horn study revealed that both city and country smokers far outdistance their nonsmoking neighbors in deaths from lung cancer. The investigators did discover that smokers in large cities, the centers of air pollution, have a significantly greater incidence of lung cancer than their country cousins. Yet, the city nonsmoker does not run a significantly greater risk of lung cancer than the country nonsmoker.

Earlier, a joint American and Italian study of lung-cancer rates in Venice, Italy, and Reykjavik, Iceland, cities selected for their virtual freedom from motor vehicle and industrial air pollution, demonstrated that lung cancer thrives along with tobacco consumption in the absence of air pollution. In Venice, where apparently more tobacco is smoked than in any other city in Italy, the investigators reported that lung cancer was the leading cancer-killer.

Thus, air pollution, while apparently adding to the already great risks of the urban smoker, is clearly insufficient by itself to account for even a fraction of lung-cancer fatalities.

When I was teaching physical education to Portland, Oregon, high school classes, I was obliged by state law to alert my pupils not only the evils of "demon rum," but also to the dangers of "tobacco heart." The instruction manual contained no clinical details or statistics—just a hideous illustration of an enlarged, misshapen heart. I rather doubted at the time the clinical verities of "tobacco heart." I now find, much to my surprise, that "tobacco heart" (in more sedate medical terms, "tobacco angina" or "nicotine angina pectoris") is a well-recognized, if minor, medical syndrome characterized by cardiac pain brought on by smoking which disappears when smoking ceases.

But even if "tobacco heart" had been merely the incarnation of a prohibitionist's nightmare, it was no more gruesome than even a restrained clinical portrait of the diseases to which the smoker is demonstrably heir.

Public health authorities naturally stress both lung cancer, because of its epidemic rise and the statistical perfection of its relationship to smoking, and coronary heart disease, which claims by far the greatest number of smoking-connected deaths. But the smoker's lungs and "accessory organs" keep many more physicians, besides cancer and coronary specialists, gainfully employed. Take emphysema, a disease which has only lately achieved just notoriety. Dr. Edward Ernest Rockey, a noted New York chest surgeon, has unceremoniously labeled emphysema a "greater crippler and killer than lung cancer." Dr. Rockey adds, moreover, that 80 per cent of the emphysema cases in this country can be traced directly to lung irritation from cigarette smoke. Emphysema is characterized by the blockage of the air passages leading out of the lungs and the consequent destruction and ballooning of the tissues at the end of the air passages.

Its effects upon the lives of its victims were graphically catalogued for the public affairs committee by Jules Saltman:

> . . . Whether he exercises or not, the victim pants for air, awake or sleeping, working or resting. He may cough continuously. His life becomes a moment-by-moment struggle to take in life-giving oxygen and expel carbon dioxide.
>
> As he steadily loses headway in the fight, the individual may have to give up work completely. Then almost all activity may stop. Next, he will need medical help to breathe —lung-clearing drugs or oxygen for a few minutes at certain times every day; then perhaps more oxygen for longer periods.

In the end, the breath of life may fail altogether. This may happen of itself, but usually it will be in the course of an acute infection—bronchitis, pneumonia, or a severe cold. It may be brought on by such an external event as a heavy, pollution-laden fog. Such episodes of acute air pollution have in the past brought death to lung cripples in London, England, in Donora, Pennsylvania, and elsewhere.

Very often it is neither the lungs nor the laboring muscles of the chest and neck that weary of their hopeless task and give up. It is the heart. The human heart is a mighty pump, but there is a limit to the unrewarding toil it can do, especially when its own muscles, along with those of the rest of the body, are starved for oxygen.

Cancer of the bladder, gastric and duodenal ulcers, bronchitis, pneumonia, influenza, pulmonary tuberculosis, thrombo-angiitis-obliterans (a disease of the arteries in which the flow of blood is impaired), tobacco amblyopia (according to the Royal College, "a rare form of blindness affecting heavy smokers"), premature delivery of infants, impaired hearing, altered metabolism, premature aging of tissues, and even accident-proneness, all have been related, with varying degrees of certitude, to smoking as cause or aggravation.

And, what of the "total risk" of smoking? I have heard enough smokers taking refuge in the conviction that "after all, lung cancer doesn't really kill very many people, probably no more than 40,000 a year. That many people die from getting out of bed and slipping on a throw rug!" There is a great variety of ingenious methods of formulating statistics on smokers' risks: the odds of the two-pack-a-day smoker living to a certain age, the comparative death rates of smokers and of nonsmokers for any given disease, the numbers of children now in school who will die of lung cancer if present levels of smoking continue. I'm not certain, however, that I really appreciated the total impact of smoking-connected disease until I heard Dr. Horn's answer to the question posed at a symposium of the Queensboro Tuberculosis and Health Association in New York: "How many Americans die annually and how many become disabled on account of their smoking habit?"

. . . What would be the situation if there were no smoking compared to what it is today? My best guess . . . is that as far as mortality is concerned *there would be somewhere in the neighborhood of 300,000 to 500,000 fewer deaths per year if it were not for smoking* . . . it represents about one sixth of the 1.8 million deaths which we have in this country. Not that these deaths would not occur . . . but they would occur later.

As far as the morbidity (incidence of illness) is concerned . . . we don't have relative figures on morbidity in general, particularly when talking about diseases like emphysema and chronic bronchitis where there is no formal reporting. But these are increasing and increasing rapidly and probably constitute at least 5 or 6 times as many people as are subject to mortality risk . . . *we probably have somewhere around a million to two million people in this country who are disabled to some degree by the effect of smoking of cigarettes.*

2

Tobacco—
"Boon to Mankind,
Bane to Zealots"

The Tobacco Institute

The tobacco industry reserved its own special reward for those scientists who had painstakingly revealed the relationship between smoking and disease. These dedicated men soon discovered what I, as a politician, had early learned: When you leave the academic cloisters and laboratories, it pays to take your brass knuckles along.

Ridicule and derision became deliberate defensive weapons in the hands of the tobacco industry public relations experts. The researchers who had discovered a close statistical relationship between smoking and disease were unceremoniously labeled "zealots," scorned as "warriors against pleasure" or "enemies of pleasure," and "peculiar." The identification of smoking as a "cancer cause" was subtly equated with past, notorious quack claims for new-found "cancer cures."

A similar fate befell the laymen, such as LeRoy Collins, the distinguished former Governor of Florida and president of the National Association of Broadcasters, who ventured to suggest that the evidence against smoking appeared conclusive. The Tobacco Institute went into an indignant funk at the effrontery of a *layman* daring to express a view on a

16

scientific matter. Such pious condemnation of Governor Collins contrasts rather dramatically with the inevitable quick-triggered press releases from Tobacco Institute *laymen* contesting the validity of each new scientific paper implicating cigarette smoke in disease.

The industry sought to identify the furor that resulted from the conclusions of the scientific community with the early superstitions and prejudices against tobacco, Thus, the Tobacco Institute recalled the past "defamation" of tobacco:

> Over several centuries the growing numbers of consumers have had to face various forms of persecution and sometimes savage punishment. They have weathered the opposition of zealous reformers, some of them hostile to all pleasures, fear-arousing campaigns of confused health zealots, and the economic penalty of excessive taxation.

The critic of tobacco who was not himself a smoker or who had given up smoking was charged with displaying his moralistic bias. Dr. Horn's earlier mentioned decision never to smoke again (made after he reviewed results of investigations of the correlation between cigarette smoking habits and death) serves to refute such charges.

If ever there were a rational decision, this was it. To characterize Dr. Horn and his associates as "zealots" on the basis of such a decision is arrant nonsense. As the *Christian Science Monitor* drily observed, no one doubts J. Edgar Hoover's objectivity in condemning narcotics because J. Edgar Hoover is not an opium smoker.

Dr. Horn facetiously suggests that he has found an antidote to industry charges of bias. In the fall of 1962, as Dr. Horn tells it, he was presented with an opportunity to pacify the tobacco industry. He was then in the process of transferring his family from New Jersey to the Washington, D.C., area so that he could devote himself to the development of a broad program of cancer control for the Department of Health, Education and Welfare.

The Horn family is devoted to rural living and reconciled to long-distance commuting. Therefore on his arrival in Washington Dr. Horn began canvassing the Maryland and Virginia countrysides for a suitably rustic residence. One day, as he was surveying a rambling Maryland farm, the realtor, pressing to close the deal, announced with a flourish that the leasehold entailed an extra bonus: the tenant would acquire a prized 3-acre tobacco allotment. This generous offer bemused the good doctor, and he declined it reluctantly. But he enjoys speculating that the acquisition of a tobacco allotment—and therein a vested interest in the tobacco industry—might have served, in the minds of tobacco men, to cancel his alleged bias as an ex-smoker.

Though I ceased believing in witches and goblins and the like when I was a young girl in Tillamook, Oregon, I confess that my study of the tobacco problem has greatly shaken my disbelief. How is one to explain the extraordinary frequency with which some unidentified force has intervened to prevent the public from learning about the hazards of smoking, without concluding that the tobacco industry is protected by a benign fairy godfather?

Even for the faithful believer, the tobacco industry must seem as unlikely a recipient for the good offices of a good fairy as can be imagined. Yet, take the odd experience of a distinguished government scientist who was asked to join in a 1-hour filmed network television program on cancer. He chose to address himself to the problem of smoking and cancer, whereupon he was allotted 2 minutes to speak. He decided to let a British poster depicting a smoldering cigarette whose twisting string of smoke spelled out, in ghostly white letters, "Cancer," deliver his message for him within this time limitation. The producers of the show were suitably apologetic when it appeared that his segment of the show—and only his segment—had been ruined in the developing.

On another occasion, the editor of a pharmaceutical magazine authored a ringing editorial condemning the role of tobacco in disease. Fearful that his editorial might be tampered
with, he insisted upon seeing the galley proofs before the
issue went to press. The proofs were satisfactory, but during
the hours intervening before the magazine was printed, his
editorial was garbled in such a way as to distort his message.

This fairy godfather's protective umbrella evidently extends
even over Wall Street, for a similar incident occurred when
the newsletter of a New York brokerage house blandly informed the investing public that the Public Health Service
did not consider smoking injurious to health. When the error
was brought to its attention, the horrified brokerage house
declared that some unseen hand had disturbed the typo-
graphical process.

The fairy's deft touch could also be seen in the experience
of the author of a tract that declared in manuscript that a
certain class of smokers was three times as likely to succumb
to lung cancer as the nonsmokers. No sooner had the presses
dried than it was discovered that during printing the risk of
the smoker had shrunk to only *twice* that of the nonsmoker.

Congressman Blatnik of Minnesota, depicting the excesses
of cigarette advertising in an essay for *Harper's*, discovered
that there is no Congressional immunity from the mischief
of the sprite. One set of the galley proofs for his article disappeared, presumably destined to enlighten and forewarn
some curious souls.

A few years ago, a newspaper report heralded the arrival of
a newly perfected "tobaccoless" cigarette. To offset the un-
pleasant fact that his product was relatively tasteless, the
developer of the tobaccoless cigarette attempted to promote
it by the use of advertisements somberly portraying the hazards of tobacco cigarettes and suggesting that the tobaccoless
cigarette, although a dubious treat, might obviate the necessity for future treatment. Unfortunately for his ill-fated ven-

ture, no prominent newspaper, magazine, or broadcaster could be induced to accept such advertising, and the tobaccoless cigarette joined the Edsel as an economic casualty of the 1950's. It was certainly great good fortune (or supernatural intervention) for the tobacco industry that these ads were uniformly rejected by the advertising media; their dreary message thus was effectively suppressed.

You may recall the earlier discussion of Dr. Cardon, whose research into the carcinogenic properties of cigarette tars was partially financed by tobacco company funds, and whose reward for discovering that notorious carcinogen, 3,4-benzpyrene in tobacco smoke was an abrupt halt to further funds from that source. Dr. Cardon's associate, James Rand, told a Congressional committee that they were forced to publish their findings in the *British Journal of Cancer* because they were unable to find an American publication "any place in this country" willing to publish their findings.

The godfather, a shrewd student of human nature, also delivered to the press an impressive object lesson in the hazards of publishing articles on the hazards of smoking. For 28 years the *Reader's Digest* was a faithful and uncomplaining client of a leading advertising agency, Batten, Barton, Durstine and Osborn. Also prominent in the BBD&O stable of clients was the American Tobacco Company, an even better (or at least bigger) client, whose estimated annual advertising expenditures of $22 million dwarfed the *Reader's Digest's* paltry $1.25 million.

The July 1957 *Reader's Digest* contained a frank and uncompromising article discussing the state of the medical evidence against smoking, with particular reference to the filter tip. On July 17, 1957 BBD&O decided that it no longer found *Reader's Digest* a suitable client. The 28-year marriage was thereupon unilaterally dissolved. At the time certain skeptical souls suggested that American Tobacco was motivated by the desire to punish *Reader's Digest* through its advertising agency and to demonstrate the muscle of an $8 billion industry scorned.

The years 1953 and 1954 were not happy ones for the to-bacco industry, for people were coming to believe that smoking was harmful. Not even concentrated blinking was going to make the health spectre disappear. The upward curve of ciga-rette sales, which had remained impervious to war and depres-sion, leveled off and even declined slightly. While the "Eisen-hower boom" sent stock market prices spiraling to new highs, tobacco shares wavered at previous levels. And casting a long and gloomy shadow were the pending Hammond-Horn and Dorn population studies.

Yet cool heads among the public-relations wise labored and brought forth a counter-offensive weapon with which to slay the smoking and health dragon: the Tobacco Industry Re-search Committee.

The creation of the TIRC, the brainchild of the resource-ful public-relations firm of Hill and Knowlton, was a stroke of ingenuity. By offering as bait millions of dollars of sorely needed research funds, the industry was able to attract sci-entists of unimpeachable integrity to serve on a nine-man Scientific Advisory Board. As responsible as these nine men were, they nevertheless served the industry's purpose of asso-ciating eminent scientists with the industry position that the relationship between smoking and disease had not yet been proved.

But that was not all. The industry gesture of sponsoring research on a grand scale was exploited as a token of the industry's true concern for the welfare of humanity—even cigarette-smoking humanity. Finally, the TIRC furnished a mechanism by which millions of dollars could be spread among research institutions to purchase (albeit subtly and indirectly) good will for the tobacco industry throughout the scientific community.

As of the present time, the TIRC has been dramatically successful in achieving all of these objectives. As for the original express purpose of the TIRC, the discovery of the relationship between smoking and health—well, in 1957 Dr. Ernest L. Wynder of the famed Sloan-Kettering Institute of Cancer Research had this to say about the results of TIRC-financed research:

> I am all in favor of the tobacco industry supporting research in this country. If they spent $2 million to further research in cancer or the tobacco-cancer problem, it is all so much the better.
>
> But I was a little discouraged if [sic] after 2½ years Dr. Little publishes his first report, after spending perhaps $2 million, and reported that they found very little.
>
> I am sure that the director of my institute, after I had spent that much money on research and after 2½ years, and I had to report I found practically nothing, would be a little bit unhappy.

At last count the TIRC had spent $5.65 million of research funds without producing any significant accretion to our knowledge of the relationship of smoking to health. TIRC's annual research funds, incidentally, represent less than 1 per cent of the industry's $170 million annual advertising outlay.

Tobacco men see themselves as a last outpost of rugged individualism and competitive ardor (except, of course, competition in price, which appears to be unfashionable). Adversity, however, can forge unity in the most disparate individuals. Thus, in 1958 the tobacco industry encased itself in a single suit of armor to do battle with the enemy, and the Tobacco Institute, of which I have made earlier mention, was born.

The Institute represents companies manufacturing 99 per cent of the cigarettes, chewing tobacco, and snuff (yes, snuff) produced in the United States today. It draws its sustenance from the companies in relation to the relative share of the market which each occupies, so that the two large giants of the industry, American and Reynolds, dominate.

Public relations is the Institute's chief function, as it provides a united industry voice in dampening public criticism of smoking.

This is not to say that there has not been diversity in the response of tobacco men to the evidence against smoking. Several of the companies, in particular P. Lorillard, though loath to admit publicly a relationship between smoking and health, have devoted considerable effort toward the development of effective filters or "safer" tobaccos. American and Reynolds, however, have steadfastly maintained that the development of filters itself stands as an implied admission that raw smoke is harmful. Out of fear that disunity in the industry might result in the collapse of tobacco's house altogether, American and Reynolds, through the Institute, have demanded public fealty to the industry line: "There is no proof of any hazard in smoking and, therefore, no need for 'safer' cigarettes." The Institute has thus served to nip in the bud any such insubordination as the 1958 full-page ad taken in a Canadian newspaper by Rothman's of Pall Mall (producers of a Canadian cigarette), acknowledging the conclusiveness of the evidence against smoking, while touting their own filter-tip brand as prophylactic.

Among the more imaginative schemes of the Tobacco Institute has been the current campaign to glorify tobacco's role in American history and to suggest by inference that an antitobacco stand is un-American. Thus, the Institute proudly recounts George Washington's plea: "If you can't send money, send tobacco," as well as General Pershing's answer to the question, "You ask me what we need to win this war and I answer, tobacco as much as bullets." If anything, these two grudging tributes to tobacco are tributes only to its addictive qualities.

Besides freely distributing copies of a magnificently illustrated historical treatise entitled, *Tobacco and Americans,* the Tobacco Institute last year promoted a glamorous celebration of tobacco's "350th year," with a festival at Jamestown commemorating the shipment of the first tobacco crop from the Jamestown Colony to England. The festival, replete with an alluring Pocahontas and cigar-smoking John Rolfe, was a smashing success and very well publicized. What red-blooded American could thenceforth dare to slander this most American of businesses?

There is, of course, no denying tobacco's romantic origins. They are, nevertheless, irrelevant in the dialogue concerning the present health implications of the smoking habit. After all, the village blacksmith represented the historical American ideal of the honest, independent craftsman, yet his romantic image failed to delay his departure from the American scene.

Another device to insinuate acceptance of tobacco as a homey, friendly product is the free distribution by the Institute of little kits to enable the young science fan to grow his own (nonsmokable) tobacco varieties from seed. There is, of course, little harm in a science lesson on the cultivation of tobacco seeds. Still, I wonder if the Institute was motivated in this venture solely by a selfless interest in the advancement of science.

The Institute has proved itself a veritable Pollyanna in finding vindication for tobacco where the less acutely attuned might not have found vindication at all. This predilection was wryly noted by *Commonweal:*

> When Pope Pius XII recently suggested to the Jesuits that they give up smoking, it never occurred to us that the tobacco industry would care much one way or the other. There are, after all, only about thirty-three thousand Jesuits in the world, and the effect of total abstinence from tobacco by all members of the Society of Jesus would hardly be very substantial. But with all the talk about lung cancer these days,

the industry is apparently very public-relations conscious, and the Pope's remarks did not go unnoticed.

Writing in *United States Tobacco Journal* (founded, incidentally, in 1874 by Oscar Hammerstein I), editor William G. Reddan is reassuring. There are and have always been, he notes, people who violently oppose the use of tobacco on moral grounds—"fanatics," according to *Tobacco Journal* —but the Pope is not one of them. Quite the contrary, in fact. The Jesuits have a way of life that "is traditionally stricter than other segments of the clergy or the laity in general," the editorial said. "Actually the papal comments are in effect an endorsement of smoking as a source of pleasure for those not dedicated to a life of complete mortification or penance or sacrifice. That means, in other words, that smoking—insofar as the Pope is concerned—is a legitimate and wholesome means of human gratification, the voluntary avoidance of which makes life a little harder physically." The Pope's remarks therefore did not constitute an attack on the use of tobacco on moral grounds; instead, "the papal advice was rendered merely as a form of counsel or guidance to the members of clerical orders seeking to achieve a more rigorous spiritual life."

Got that straight, you non-Jesuits?

Somewhere in this great country there undoubtedly exists a group of people who firmly believe that the sun and all the planets revolve dutifully about the earth. The group may even have a publicity officer who prepares press releases condemning modern science for promulgating the heresy that the earth revolves around the sun. Of course, the likelihood that any of these press releases, no matter how eloquent, would find their way into print in any of the nation's newspapers or magazines, is undeniably dim.

Yet the spokesmen for the tobacco industry, promoting a point of view which in the minds of most medical and scientific authorities is as unsubstantiated as the earth-centered theory of the universe, find their way into print with remarkable regularity. Like the tail of a kite, no story about the risk of smoking goes anywhere without a tobacco industry rebuttal trailing along behind. This practice was the subject of a magnificently indignant letter to *The New York Times* by John Kenneth Galbraith, then Professor at Harvard University and recently Ambassador to India, following the publication in the *Times* of an article which coupled news of a new scientific paper concerning the harmful effects of smoking with the most recent version of the Tobacco Institute's disclaimer:

> On August 7 you published a report on the findings of Dr. Harold F. Dorn, a Government research scientist, on the relation of smoking to the death rate. The study, according to your account, covered nearly 200,000 veterans whose smoking habits had been ascertained before their death. It found that the death rate for heavy cigarette smokers was about twice that for nonsmokers. The incidence of lung cancer, an important and usually mortal affliction, was sixteen times as great for heavy smokers as for nonsmokers.
>
> The auspices under which the study was conducted, the United States Government, commands respect. The sample of 200,000 men suggests the formidable scale of the enterprise. Few would wish to challenge the bearing of the conclusions on an important problem of the public health. If from some wholly improbable sampling bias the figure for lung cancer were twice too high, an incidence eight times as great for heavy smokers would be impressive.
>
> Your news story, nonetheless, carried several paragraphs of a statement by Timothy V. Hartnett, the head of something called the Tobacco Industry Research Committee which said it wasn't so. . . .
>
> . . . In the news story, while you give considerably more space to Dr. Dorn than to Mr. Hartnett, you treat the statements of both with equal respect. Does not this seeming impartiality mean, in fact, that you are allowing Mr. Hartnett to use you for his own purposes in a rather outrageous way?
>
> For years now the tobacco industry has been capping careful

research reports with these unsupported denials. I certainly wouldn't suggest that you suppress Mr. Hartnett, but shouldn't you remind your readers of these past denials and the predictable character of this one? Indeed, shouldn't you make it wholly clear that you are not equating the work of a careful researcher extending over years with the press releases of an industry spokesman?

It is bad enough when, as here, a story is distorted. Even more reprehensible are the occasions upon which a publisher considering distortion insufficient sacrifice to propitiate his advertiser, actually engages in affirmative misrepresentation. Walter Goodman, in the June 1960 *Redbook*, described the distasteful circumstances of one such incident.

> Some years ago, for example, *Cosmopolitan* assigned a team of reputable writers to do an article on environmental causes of cancer. After receiving the manuscript, the magazine's editors asked the writers to add a statement to the effect that the cigarette-lung cancer link was discredited. The writers refused, and insisted that their names be taken off the story.

> Two paragraphs written by someone else were inserted, stating in effect that "the cigarette seems to be all but exonerated" as a cause of lung cancer, and the article was printed in May 1956, with a fictitious byline.

More sinister than the practice of striking a false balance (and more difficult to prove) is the practice of killing, or at least maiming, stories which might cause offense to cigarette advertisers. At least one such incident of recent vintage can be fully documented, however.

During the summer of 1962, a Washington correspondent for a New York newspaper predicted in a signed article that President Kennedy would shortly endorse the statement of Surgeon General Burney that smoking was a causal factor in lung cancer. It was a reasonable guess at the time. I, myself, had earlier bravely forecast on the floor of the Senate that President Kennedy would be forced to take that position. As it turned out, of course, we were both wrong. Nevertheless, the prediction was in the realm of a responsible educated guess.

The first edition of his paper carrying this story had no sooner appeared on the newsstands than the reporter received an apoplectic long-distance call from his editor, who, in turn, had been visited in wrath by the publisher (who, presumably, in turn had been visited by an advertiser or agency). The editor demanded to know the source for the prediction. The reporter refused to disclose his source, answering only that he had consulted several persons in the Administration who might be expected to have some insight into the President's thinking. The article was unceremoniously yanked from subsequent editions of the paper.

The hapless reporter had not heard the last of it. For the next several weeks, he was harassed by one phone call after another from New York and was finally forced to prepare a memorandum baring his breast in justification of his story. It was, he related, a degrading experience. But more than that: *It was the first and only time in the many years during which he had been a Washington correspondent that he had ever been questioned on the source of a story.*

3

Advertising
and Promotion

George Washington Hill was the patriarch of modern "hard sell" cigarette advertising. His was the flamboyance and marketing genius that catapulted Lucky Strike to the first position among modern cigarettes. So complete was his identification with his product that tobacco plants flourished in the garden of his home, and radios in every room bathed him in the sound of his own cigarette commercials. When asked to assess the impact of advertising upon the growth of cigarette consumption, Hill answered: "The impetus of those great advertising campaigns . . . *built* the cigarette business. . . ." (Italics are mine.)

Other early cigarette industry leaders were equally generous in crediting advertising with profound influence upon the over-all consumption of cigarettes. S. Clay Williams maintained, ". . . if we were to discontinue advertising of our brands . . . you would find a sloughing off of the volume of consumption of tobacco products in that form. . . ."

Printer's Ink, a magazine of the advertising industry, several years ago nominated advertising as "the one feature which has contributed more than any other single factor to the enormous growth of the cigarette industry."

But today's cigarette or ad agency executive is uncharacteristically modest about advertising's role. He insists that his advertising's only function is to induce the confirmed smoker to abandon his present brand for the advertiser's own. "Isn't it true," you ask the cigarette man, "that you are now employing a potent arsenal of motivational and psychological weapons to recruit new smokers and stiffen the backbones of confirmed but skittish smokers?" "Not so," he replies, "our ads are just about flavor and taste." And if you dare to suggest that his ads are calculated to convince the adolescent non-smoker that smoking is a badge of maturity, socially desirable, and an essential concomitant of the good life, you provoke only anguished disclaimers.

I suggest that no one who takes a searching look at the history of cigarette advertising, or even a random sampling of the latest round of cigarette ads and commercials, can accept at face value the industry's protestations. I suspect that G. W. Hill and his contemporaries were being more candid with us when they described the cigarette industry as a house that advertising built, and that advertising is, indeed, a key to the continued maintenance of that house in good repair, despite the blizzard of medical evidence incriminating smoking. Moreover, there is every evidence that we have witnessed a deliberate industry effort to employ the most modern techniques of advertising to construct a teen-age wing to its house.

The American smoker during the '30's and '40's could have been forgiven for confusing his favorite brand of cigarettes with the latest wonder drug. The industry's response to early intimations of the potential harm in smoking was thenceforth, in the words of Business Week, to "sell health." Thus, in the early '30's cigarette ads blossomed forth with a new medicinal flavor. Remember such mottos as: "Not a cough in

a carload" (Old Gold), "Not one single case of throat irritation due to smoking Camels," "The throat-tested cigarette"
(Philip Morris), "Nature in the raw is seldom mild," "It's
toasted" (Luckies), and "Nose, throat, and accessory organs
not adversely affected by smoking Chesterfields."

Not content simply to negate the hazards of smoking the
sponsor's brand, the ads virtually prescribed cigarettes as a
tonic for all the ills of modern Americans. For nervousness:
"Are you a key juggler? Watch out for jangled nerves." For
the stomach: "For digestion's sake, smoke Camels . . . stim-
ulates the flow of digestive fluids . . . increases alkalinity."
In the words of Dr. Michael Shimkin, cancer specialist and
jaundiced connoisseur of cigarette advertising, ". . . the medicinal era of cigarettes culminated with the 1936 identification of smoking with doctors." And on every panel and
channel, the soothing presence of the white-frocked man of
medicine confided that "More doctors smoke Camels than
any other cigarette."

By the mid-1950's, however, cigarette advertising degener-
ated into a medical Olympics of competing tar and nicotine
claims. Filters outbid each other in claiming the removal of
whatever it was that was "allegedly" harmful in smoke.

What had once been faintly amusing to some of us, distasteful to others, took on a more sinister aspect in the light of
the new evidence relating smoking to death. The Federal
Trade Commission, which had sought unsuccessfully to limit
the industry's medical posturing through Commission Advertising "guides," made menacing moves toward tighter policing of advertising (see Chapter 6). The American Medical
Association, too, took belated notice of the cigarette industry's misappropriation of the medical profession, labeling
cigarette ads "a cheap attempt to mislead" and banning cigarette advertisements in its own publications.

The cigarette industry was ripe either for an injection of
sanity and morality in its advertising or for new ways to

Christmas

1926

"PLAYER'S
ALWAYS
PLEASE"

A Casket
of happy
Memories

This casket contains
100 plain and 50 cork tipped
PLAYER'S *Medium* NAVY CUT CIGARETTES
150 CIGARETTES FOR 7'6ᴰ

PLAYER'S
NAVY CUT

Sept. 15, 1946

"...sound
as a bell"

More Doctors Smoke Camels
than any other Cigarette

CAMELS *Costlier Tobaccos*

continue hawking its wares without falling prey to rigid regulation or outright censorship. Its choice was not long in coming.

The growing revulsion of the FTC, the AMA, and the public at the cigarette advertisers' excesses was shared by the new band of advertising experts: the practitioners of the science (or sport) of motivational research. They were offended, of course, not because cigarette advertising had become unconscionable but because they considered it ineffectual. The cigarette industry must remain eternally grateful to the *Chicago Tribune* for financing a revolutionary study by a Chicago consulting firm with the businesslike name of Social Research, Inc. In a report entitled "Cigarettes, Their Role and Function" its results were publicized.

The psychologists of Social Research tore away at the smoker's façade of rationality. They concluded that the industry's strident health claims intimidated the timid smoker while failing to appeal to his deep psychological motivations. These hidden motivations were pictured as varied and colorful, to say the least. For some, the psychologists insisted, cigarette smoking is a reward for hard or creative work, for real (or imagined) accomplishment. Others smoked to be sociable ("Cigarettes facilitate social interaction"). Still others, to conform. To many, smoking was a badge of poise and sophistication, of daring or liberation. But the report reached a conclusion that was a call to arms for even the least imaginative advertising man:

> Americans smoke—and in increasing numbers—to prove that they are virile, to demonstrate their energy, vigor, and potency. This is a psychological satisfaction *sufficient to overcome health fears.* (My italics.)

He had obviously been wasting his talents attempting to fight the fire of health fears with the water of health claims.

The secret lay in distracting the smoker with a hotter fire, catering to his need to prove his virility.

No cigarette company grabbed this motivational bait with as much enthusiasm as the makers of Marlboro. Marlboro ("mild as May") had been a staid, feminine member of the Philip Morris menagerie. The makers of Marlboro paused just long enough to absorb Social Research, Inc.'s message of masculinity before they were off on the advertising campaign that Vance Packard called "a spectacular transvestitism." The Marlboro tattoo became synonymous with modern advertising's coming of age in a psychologically oriented world. Marlboro reaped bouquets from the motivational researchers. Packard quotes Pierre Martineau, Research Director of the *Chicago Tribune*, and a motivational research aficionado, as stating that the Marlboro tattoo struck "right in the heart of some core meanings of smoking: masculinity, adulthood, vigor, and potency."

To this day, cigarette ads and commercials tumble over each other, straining to identify cigarettes with each of the manly virtues. We continue to be subjected to a ceaseless display of smokers engaged in the most virile of occupations— shortly returned from conquering the icy North or outer space or the campus queen—while the copy crows "every inch a man's smoke." There is little subtlety in the appeal to masculinity of the rhetorical question, "Who put the men in menthol?" And what on earth does a cigarette taste like when it has "swagger"?

The industry turned from the wisdom of Social Research, Inc. to seek out the guidance of like-minded prophets. Chief among these is Dr. Ernest E. Dichter, hailed, variously, as "the high priest of hidden persuasion" and "Mr. Mass Motivations himself."

Brooding down upon the Hudson River from its perch atop Prickly Pear Hill in Croton-on-Hudson, New York, stands the 26-room fieldstone castle of Dr. Dichter's Institute for Motivational Research. For $500 a day Dr. Dichter will identify for you the "irrational, unconscious, unknown" motivations driving people to buy your product. He will, moreover, instruct you in the most efficient means of exploiting these motivations.

Cigarette manufacturers and their advertising agencies have not, to my knowledge, publicized the fact that they have sought Dr. Dichter's services in solving their marketing problems. Dr. Dichter, however, has not been equally bashful.

In a moment of candor, Dr. Dichter once revealed the character of the relationship between the cigarette advertiser and his motivational research consultant: "He [the advertiser] is not interested in knowing per se that cigarette smoking is an oral satisfaction. . . . What he needs to know is how to use such an appeal and how to talk about it in his merchandising approach and in his advertising." Dr. Dichter thinks it fortunate that psychologists are being called upon to perform such tasks. He considers assignments such as this a "unique opportunity" for the social scientists to function as "social engineers."

To his eager clients, Dr. Dichter served up a dubious porridge of Freudian psychiatry:

> In cigarette ads . . . the combination of filter and pleasure appeals means an attempt to communicate with both the rational "ego," bent on preserving health, and with the "id," clamoring for all kinds of sensuous gratification. A third kind of appeal which currently stresses the sociability of smokers even appeals to "superego." Here, one emotion, "cigarettes is a vice," is combatted by another one: "cigarettes create a bond among people."

Here was the industry's salvation according to Dichter: Make health claims if you want, but be sure also to tug at the smoker's id and superego.

Once bitten by the Freudian bug, advertisers displayed little restraint in pandering to the darker corners of the mind in the attempt to overpower the smoker's health fears. They exploited the "oral indulgence" function of smoking by picturing sensuous close-ups of lips and fingers fondling cigarettes.

And they discovered sex. Dr. Dichter himself described the slogan, "Don't filter your fun—like your pleasures big," the Chesterfield theme, as "Conscious attempts to send a latent sexual message enclosed in the language of manifest innocence."

The preoccupation of cigarette advertisers with Freudian symbolism was the object of a delightful cartoon in the *London Spectator* that appeared during the flurry of public reaction to the Royal College of Physicians report. Two troubled ad men are speaking. One, shrugging, says resignedly, "O.K., we'll drop the sex angle and play up the death wish."

Even if the psychological twists and manipulations of the motivational research enthusiast are ineffectual, as many respected psychologists believe, there remains at least one critical role which cigarette advertising continues to perform in aggravating the problem of the confirmed smoker: cigarette advertisements provide reassurance to the smoker, not because of what they say but simply because of their continued unrestricted publication.

Can you imagine the following sunny, four-color ad radiating from the pages of *Time* or *Life?* A handsome young couple is pictured standing on the front steps of the young lady's fashionable, Manhattan brownstone home. Before taking his leave, the young man is whispering into his beloved's ear the tender advice: "Take thalidomide for a sedative that gentles you to sleep for the longer length of the winter night."

Outrageous? Of course, yet the ad would be guilty of neither false claims nor misrepresentation. Thalidomide is truly a potent sleeping potion. It isn't habit-forming and has

no apparent harmful side effects—on the *user*. Indeed, in
Germany, where it was first marketed, it proved so effective a
sedative that it was fast becoming a best-selling pill when
Germany harvested its first crop of thalidomide-deformed
babies.

Why would we then be shocked at the publication of such
an advertisement? Because we know that many people would
respond by buying and using thalidomide, believing that if
thalidomide were truly hazardous, agencies such as the Food
and Drug Administration and the Federal Trade Commission
would prohibit its advertisement and sale.

I can see little distinction between my hypothetical thalidomide advertisement and the present generation of cigarette
advertisements. Even in the absence of overt health claims, the
mere continuation of massive cigarette advertising campaigns
acts as an implied assurance or warranty of the safety of cigarettes to a people who have learned to expect that what is
advertised may not really be a bargain but will, at least, not
kill you.

Cigarette advertising affords the cigarette smoker a conven-
ient rationalization for his addiction, for he is able to say to
himself, "If smoking were really dangerous, the government
would surely put a halt to all that advertising." That smokers
have, in fact, thus reacted is confirmed by Dr. Horn, whose
interviews for the American Cancer Society have frequently
revealed that smokers rely on the continued existence of cigarette advertisements as proof that "smoking could not be all
that bad."

It is interesting to note, too, that the psychologists of
Social Research, Inc., stressed the importance of advertising
in allaying the smoker's fears. "Advertising makes cigarettes
respectable, and is thus reassuring," they stated.

There are few people in public life for whom I harbor such
unqualified admiration as LeRoy Collins, former Governor

of Florida, now chief executive and staunch conscience of the National Association of Broadcasters. He is, as commentator Edward P. Morgan perceptively characterized him, "bold, civilized, strong-minded."

On November 19, 1962 at Portland, Oregon, Governor Collins lashed out angrily at the curtain of silence with which the broadcasting industry had cloaked its role in propagating cigarette advertising. Governor Collins told his audience of broadcasters:

> It is my personal view that our [radio and television] codes should be much more than sets of legalistic standards and delineations of good taste and estimated public tolerance. I think the codes should serve as a broadcast conscience as well. Under them and to them, the individual broadcaster and all related enterprises should be able to look for, and find, ethical and moral leadership.

> For example, if we are honest with ourselves, we cannot ignore the mounting evidence that tobacco provides a serious hazard to health. Can we either in good conscience ignore the fact that progressively more and more of our high-school age (and lower) children are now becoming habitual cigarette smokers? The most recent statistics I have seen point out that 20 per cent of boys have started smoking in the ninth grade, and almost 30 per cent of all girls smoke before they are graduated from high school. We also know that this condition is being made continually worse under the promotional impact of advertising designed primarily to influence young people.

> Certainly the moral responsibility rests first on the tobacco manufacturer. Certainly it also rests on the advertising agencies. Certainly it also rests on the outstanding sports figures who permit their hero status to be prostituted.

> It is also true that broadcasting, and other advertising media, cannot be expected to sit in judgment and vouch for the propriety of all advertising presented to the public over their facilities.

But where others have persistently failed to subordinate their profit motives to the higher purpose of the general good health of our young people, then I think the broadcaster should make corrective moves on his own. This we could do under code amendments, and I feel we should proceed to do so, not because we are required to, but because a sense of moral responsibility demands it.

The reaction from the industry was immediate, anguished and depressing. *The New York Times* reported that the major networks and other broadcasters were tumbling head over heels in their scramble to disassociate themselves from the Governor's remarks. This unedifying spectacle distressed me so that I was moved to address the following letter to Robert Kintner, President of the National Broadcasting Company:

Few industries have had the good fortune to attract a leader with the foresight and courage of LeRoy Collins. But surely no industry has responded so lamely to such leadership as the broadcasting industry.

When Governor Collins recently pleaded for a self-imposed broadcasters' curb on the tasteless and immoral excesses of child-oriented tobacco advertising, NBC acted with remarkable agility to reject his proposal out of hand. Your company stated: "NBC does not share Governor Collins' views."

I am curious as to which of his views NBC disowns. Do you deny that the broadcaster may have the responsibility to subordinate profit to "the higher purpose of the general good health of our young people"? Such a denial would, no doubt, come as a distinct surprise to the FCC.

Or do you disagree that tobacco commercials are "designed primarily to influence young people"? Can there be any serious doubt that the thrust of today's cigarette commercials is to associate the successful transition from childhood to maturity, social bliss, athletic prowess, even "Americanism" with cigarette smoking?

Or do you not believe that there is "mounting evidence that cigarettes provide a serious hazard to health"? If you do not, then you join the tobacco industry in an increasingly narrow circle of skeptics whose profits seem to serve as blinders to their judgment.

On October 26, 1961, after an exhaustive 2-year review of the scientific literature, the Royal College of Physicians reported unequivocally, "Cigarette smoking is a cause of lung cancer, and bronchitis, and probably contributes to the development of coronary heart disease and various other less-common diseases. It delays healing of gastric and duodenal ulcers."

In this country, the Public Health Service recently reiterated its conclusion "that the weight of evidence at present shows that smoking—particularly cigarette smoking—is a principal reason for the rising death rate from lung cancer in the past 30 years."

In England, both the tobacco industry and broadcasting industry responded vigorously to this indictment. The tobacco companies voluntarily eliminated cigarette commercials before 9 P.M. (In this country nearly 60 per cent of the cigarette commercials appear before 9 P.M.), and the independent television authority moved to prohibit all advertisements "which could reasonably be taken to make a special appeal to young people."

Governor Collins has challenged you to react in the best traditions of industrial self-regulation. He has given you the opportunity to convince a disturbed and skeptical public of your good faith and responsibility. He did not, after all, recommend the total abolition of cigarette advertising, but asked only that you eliminate the calculated seduction of children to the smoking habit. Should you fail to act, it is inevitable that the need for regulation will eventually find its expression in a Congressional mandate.

Mr. Kintner, the President of NBC, was gracious enough to reply to my letter and to attempt to answer my criticisms and those of Collins'. Unfortunately, I found his answers, par-

ticularly with respect to the charge that cigarette commercials were essentially child-directed, unsatisfactory. He wrote:

> So far as the commercials themselves are concerned, they
> neither appear in programs designed specifically for children,
> nor in our judgment do they make special appeals to chil-
> dren. On the contrary, the typical approach of these com-
> mercials, we believe, is general in theme and competitive in
> direction, depicting the pleasure of smoking and emphasizing
> the particular virtues of the advertised brand. We do not
> regard the appearance of sports figures in cigarette commer-
> cials—the only specific Governor Collins mentioned—as rep-
> resenting a special appeal to children, any more than their
> appearance in commercials for various other products, such
> as hair lotion; these personalities are universally popular fig-
> ures throughout the population, particularly with men, and
> it seems to us that their use in commercials is normal and
> proper. We would ourselves reject tobacco commercials
> that we felt were designed to appeal directly and specifically
> to children, but there has been no need to do so, since no
> such commercials have been proposed to us, nor do we think
> they are likely to be.

The suggestion, which did not originate with Mr. Kintner,
that the cigarette industry was interested only in appealing to
the confirmed smoker and not in exploiting new and un-
tapped markets for cigarettes, is unconvincing. If any proof
of the industry's appetite for new sources of revenue is necessary, the historic campaign to woo women to smoking serves
as an illuminating illustration.

P. Lorillard first dared to bait the female with its famous
1919 advertisement for Helmar cigarettes which displayed a
sweet young thing in outlandish costume set in some native
New Yorker's image of an oriental backdrop, looking, as an
unkind critic at the time noted, as if she had "never been
East of Brooklyn Borough Hall."

This feeble effort was followed by Chesterfield's emancipated vamp begging, "Blow some my way!" But the pursuit of the female smoker really commenced in earnest with the 1927 Marlboro ad which dared to suggest, "Women when they smoke at all, quickly develop discriminating taste," and there, for all the world to behold, was a Marlboro lady—on the threshold of succumbing to the cigarette "mild as May."

This historic ad provoked the following admiring comment from the trade journal "*Advertising and Selling*":

> In its new progressive consciousness America of today has little use for outworn prejudices, and these are being shelved automatically in the triumphant march of progress. . . . It requires little imagination to conceive of the potential market lying in this direction only waiting for the intensive cultivation of the advertiser.

It was shortly thereafter that George Washington Hill conceived his great contribution to the literature of female-directed advertising, "Reach for a Lucky instead of a sweet."

Mr. Kintner, however, is aware of no evidence that cigarette commercials are today "designed to appeal directly and specifically to children." Perhaps there is some other explanation for the frantic emphasis on youth in cigarette commercials. *Monocle* magazine, in a delightful parody on cigarette advertising, quotes a despairing account executive for the "Turkish-American Tobacco Company":

> "We only show the handsomest, young college football tackles kissing beauty queens," the account executive said. "That doesn't help our health image. Subconsciously people are asking: Why are there only young folks in the commercials? Could it be that nobody who smokes our brand lives long enough to appear in our commercials."

And it is quite true that the industry has not yet adopted the forthright appeal to children which *Monocle* suggests will become the New Frontier of cigarette advertising. Such as:

The way to enjoy smoke, Every inch a boy's smoke.

or

The best taste you ever did smoke, Every inch a kid's smoke.

or even

The best tasting mild smoke, Every inch a child's smoke, Every inch a child's cigarette.

Yet it is, I should think, an undisputed fact that the psychological needs boldly exploited by current cigarette advertising are precisely the needs that are felt most strongly, albeit not solely, by adolescents.

The Social Research Study makes no bones about it.

Very prominent is the idea of maturity. Practically everyone recognizes that one has to be, "old enough to smoke"—that teen-agers want to smoke to be grown-up.

Smoking cigarettes expresses more than just the idea of maturity—it *actually refers to virile maturity.* . . .

Young people who smoke are trying to be older. . . . Smoking cigarettes is a symbol that testifies to productive maturity (whether actually the case or not).

Social Research also identified the adolescent's need to conform as a "recurrent and basic . . . social meaning of smoking cigarettes."

The more people there are who smoke, the stronger is the pressure for others to submit to this custom. And to refuse implies some kind of aloofness. The pressure of conformity is especially strong for adolescents.

One need hardly be an expert in motivational research to discover that the glorification of a game of tennis—followed by a smoke, or of a brisk swim—followed by a smoke, or of a romantic encounter—followed by a smoke, has a "special appeal to young people." As Dr. Shimkin has said, "Cigarette advertising equates smoking cigarettes with bravery, sexual virility and social status, and in view of this campaign it is little wonder that so many youngsters smoke."

Nor is there any question that athletes are idolized and romanticized by adolescents and that these emotions are exploited by the use of the star athlete testimonial—a technique that *Changing Times*, in a provocative review of cigarette advertising, labeled "Casey at the ash tray."

I received a particularly poignant letter from a gentleman in McClure, Virginia, bemoaning the effect upon his grandson of just such testimonials: "I have heard them say after watching one of these programs that they would smoke Camels because Camels' smokers make great heroes. I have heard them say, 'Now just look at Roger Maris, Mickey Mantle, Whitey Ford or what have you. He smokes Camels and you see what it has made him.' "

I am a little past the point of baseball hero-worship, but I thought fleetingly of the honored plea: "Say it ain't so—Roger, Mickey and Whitey!" More from curiosity than sorrow, I consulted the William Esty advertising agency, promoter of Camels, to see if Maris, Mantle and Ford really did puff Camels for pay. The truth is both interesting and revealing.

Roger Maris had smoked Camels contentedly both in the advertisements and off for the previous year, but had, just a month before, stopped smoking altogether. Mickey Mantle, a Camels standard bearer from 1951 to 1955, then switched to Viceroys and finally took a further step: He is now featured in the advertisements for Bantron, an anti-smoking pill.

The agency had no current intelligence on Whitey Ford's smoking habits, though the pitcher had been featured in Camels' advertising from 1953 to 1962. But in an article in the *New York World-Telegram and Sun* of May 3, 1963, celebrating his first shutout victory of the season, Ford had a warming explanation for his performance:

"This was the best I've felt for nine innings since the first game of the World Series against Cincinnati," Ford said. That's the World Series of 1961, in case you get your series opponent confused.

That means Whitey worked the entire 1962 season, not feeling just right. He figures he's got the solution for his improvement, though. "I quit smoking," he announced, no small accomplishment for a former two-pack-a-day man.

Now, there's a testimonial!

Among New York State's many colleges and universities, Cortland State Teachers College is distinguished for its production of fine physical education teachers. A distinction of somewhat less magnitude, however, was the 1961 first-place victory of the Cortland Alpha Delta Delta sorority in a contest sponsored by Philip Morris, Inc. For engineering the consumption of 1,520,000 cigarettes produced by Philip Morris and redeeming the empty packages, the girls of Alpha Delta Delta were awarded a magnificent high-fidelity phonograph.

By coincidence a young lady on my office staff was privy to the trials of one Alpha Delta, who lamented that, as the deadline for collecting packages approached, the sorority house was suffused with a crisis psychology. The continued smoking of Philip Morris brands at a breathless pace became a badge of loyalty. One girl was compelled to abandon her relatively mild filtered cigarette for the nonfiltered Philip Morris—a change which turned her a shade of near green. The sorority house was strewn with lipstick-smeared butts and massive piles of empty packages. The reluctant sister who dared to venture into the open without a cigarette dangling from her lips risked displeasure and even ostracism.

But the girls won their new hi-fi set. And Philip Morris presumably won the gratitude, if not the customer loyalty, of future physical education teachers whose enthusiasm for teaching the health hazards of smoking might be appreciably diminished.

Meanwhile, in New York City a Columbia University student was consuming a substantial segment of his bright college years by constructing a replica of the United Nations headquarters from six thousand Marlboro and Parliament boxes. To the poets among the college scholars, Liggett and Myers held out the lure of eight British Sprite sports cars to be awarded for the creative completion of a limerick, plus an offering of the bottom panels from five Chesterfield, L & M, or Oasis packages. And to sports-minded campus clairvoyants who successfully predicted the outcome of selected football games, Brown and Williamson (Viceroy, Kool, Raleigh) presented cash prizes of ten to one hundred dollars.

Buried in a *New York Times* article on the activities of the cigarette campus pitchmen was this tantalizing intelligence, "Once in California, a fire engine was awarded as a prize." I regret that the *Times*, which rarely fails us, succeeded only in whetting, not quenching, my curiosity. What college student or group could possibly have any use or desire for a fire engine (especially with Sprite sports cars on the loose)? And what pile of packages had to be amassed as its price?

The contests are only symptomatic of the umbrella spread by the cigarette companies over every conceivable form of campus activity. College newspapers once abounded in breezy cigarette ads, tailored to their very special audience. (Tobacco companies contributed a staggering 40 per cent of all national advertising placed in college newspapers.) The undergraduate who developed an understandable taste for the irreverent humor of Max Shulman could find him gaily touting Marlboros in nearly every college publication, while American Tobacco's copywriters assured the collegian that the "Important things in college life stay the same. Parties. Girls. Luckies." And, lest the point be missed, other ads discarded subtlety entirely. Typical were "Luckies—the Cigarette to start with" and "More college students smoke Luckies—than any other regular cigarette."

The Brown and Williamson Company had at least seventeen salesmen engaging their energies as Viceroy, Kool, and Raleigh Santa Clauses to the colleges. And Philip Morris picked worthy students on 166 college campuses as "campus representatives," paying each $50 a month to spread good cheer and complimentary Marlboros. No student political rally, no fraternity party, no tea for foreign students escaped the beneficence of Philip Morris.

Of course, it sometimes happens that when the contests are all won, the samples consumed, and the advertising messages burned across the consciousness of the nation's incubating youth, one or another uncooperative undergraduate still declines to smoke. But the imaginative R. J. Reynolds Tobacco Company established a program with the collegiate-sounding title of "The Line-Backer" system. Reynolds simply recruited college public information officials to insure that Camels and other company brands advertised in the college's football programs could be seen, admired, and purchased in every conceivable nook and cranny of the college. By hawking Camels from the college roof-tops, the public information officials earned the right to participate in a contest of their own with foreign cars as a reward for soliciting their students.*

* On June 20, 1963, the Tobacco Institute announced that most of the major cigarette manufacturers (apparently all but Philip Morris) had called a halt to campus advertising and promotions. And there, I hope, ends one of the sorriest episodes in American advertising history.

4

The
Public Guardians

Would you consider tobacco a product with "the capacity to produce . . . illness to man . . . through inhalation"?

I certainly would. The Federal Food and Drug Administrator would not and, indeed, does not. And since this is a definition of a "hazardous substance" contained in the Federal Hazardous Substances Labeling Act of 1960, the Administrator's disagreement relieves him of the distasteful burden—and singular opportunity—of requiring every cigarette package sold to bear a label emblazoned with the word WARNING or CAUTION in capital letters, together with a suitable statement of the principal hazards of smoking.

You may wonder that the power to regulate tobacco was not encompassed by the Food and Drug Administration's original jurisdiction over consumables. Yet, true to the quaint folkways of Washington, it was decreed quite early that tobacco, being neither food nor drug, was safely beyond the reach of the Food and Drug Administration.

Neither the first Food and Drug Act in 1906 nor its modern dress version, the Food, Drug and Cosmetic Act of 1935, pays any particular attention to tobacco, although Congress

in 1935 demonstrated its concern for the health of the public
by expressly placing chewing gum under the Commissioner's
thumb. Besides chewing gum, the Commissioner's office can
regulate the sale of any drug appearing in such official drug
lists as the United States Pharmacopoeia. Tobacco doesn't
grace the pages of the Pharmacopoeia and thus escapes the
scrutiny of the one agency of government most equipped to
oversee the sale and marketing of a product as potentially
lethal as the cigarette.

There is a political legend that tobacco was banished from
the pages of the Pharmacopoeia in exchange for the votes of
tobacco state Congressmen for the original Food and Drug
Act. It *is* a matter of record that tobacco is listed as a drug in
the 1890 edition of the Pharmacopoeia (the edition that was
current as late as 1905) and never again. That curious fact
alone lends some color of truth to this story of turn-of-the-
century legislative legerdemain.

Thus, it was not until passage of the Federal Hazardous
Substances Labeling Act in 1960 that the Food and Drug
Commissioner was offered an opportunity to attack the cigarette problem. It is an opportunity that he has thus far
avoided facing.

I am not suggesting that the Commissioner arbitrarily
ducks his responsibility by refusing to treat the cigarette as a
hazardous substance. There is, after all, scant evidence that
the sponsors of the Hazardous Substances Labeling Act ever
dreamed it might be used to regulate cigarette sales. One can
well imagine the howls of anguish from the tobacco state
Congressmen which would accompany any move by the
Commissioner to place his protective umbrella over cigarette
sales.

The Food and Drug Administration is by no means the
sole, or even the chief villain of the smoking story. Yet, the
action—or inaction—of the Food and Drug Administration
provides a fair sample of the overriding timidity and inertia

that have plagued nearly every governmental response to the smoking problem. The Public Health Service, the Federal Trade Commission, the Department of Agriculture, Congress, and, for the most part, the individual states and local governments have had a shared opportunity and obligation to aid in a constructive solution of the smoking problem. And each, to a greater or lesser degree, has rather dismally failed.

At the very bottom of the list, if one chooses to rank government agencies in the order in which they have displayed some measure of responsibility in treating the smoking problem, sits the Tobacco Division of the Department of Agriculture.

If the Food and Drug Administration has been lethargic in its response to the smoking problem, the posture of the Tobacco Division of the Department of Agriculture has been delinquent. The delicate sense of public responsibility displayed by officials of the Tobacco Division was sharply etched in the following newspaper article thoughtfully inserted by Congressman Abbitt of Virginia in the *Congressional Record* several years ago:

United States Aide Fights Cigarette Scare *
By Don Oberdorfer
WASHINGTON, JULY 8. While the Surgeon General was announcing a Government campaign against heavy smoking yesterday, another Government official was urging citizens to "sit back, relax, and smoke a cigarette."

He is Joe R. Williams, Chief of the Tobacco Division of the Agriculture Department's marketing services. He helps tobacco farmers sell their leaf.

Williams said a study of 300 years of antismoking crusades shows the attacks on tobacco usually end up by stimulating consumption.

The current antismoking campaign, touched off by a new

* *The New York Journal-American*, July 8, 1958

Government medical report on high death rates among heavy smokers, will add another few pounds to tobacco consumption, Williams predicted.

"My wife is so disturbed over the current health scare that she is now smoking twice as many cigarettes as she did a year ago," Williams said.

He traced the first attacks on tobacco to King James I of England, who wrote a book titled *A Counter Blaste to Tobacco* after the weed was popularized by Sir Walter Raleigh in 1604.

The King wrote that since Indians used tobacco smoke to cure venereal disease, no English gentleman would risk the implication by indulging in the same remedy.

In 1830, Williams recalls, educators, physicians, clergymen —and P. T. Barnum—launched a campaign on tobacco which lasted 30 years.

Horace Mann, Henry Ward Beecher, and Horace Greeley crusaded against smoking.

Tobacco was held responsible for many diseases—including cancer and insanity.

The advent of the cigarette in the 1890's brought a new antismoking crusade. Between 1895 and 1921 a total of 14 States banned the sale of cigarettes. By 1927 all of these laws were repealed.

The Agriculture Department official calls the tobacco health crusade a big smokescreen.

The Tobacco Division's substantial research facilities and budget are placed generously at the disposal of the industry. Research projects are uniformly molded to the development of only those types of tobaccos that the industry asks for, with barely a nod to the intriguing possibilities of selective cultivation of tobaccos to develop low-tar and low-nicotine varieties.

Even if we concede that the primary purpose of the Tobacco Division is to accommodate the tobacco industry, I can't believe that the interests of that industry would not be well served by the development of tobaccos that would help to remove the medical cloud from tobacco smoke. But it is apparent that neither responsibility nor leadership in this area is forthcoming from the Department of Agriculture. I cannot take leave of the Tobacco Division without noting an appalling illustration of the Division's ability to accommodate to the interests of the industry. By 1955, manufacturers who had turned to the use of filters found that they needed heavier and darker varieties of tobacco to strengthen the flavor that could be strained through the filter. The tobacco farmers, however, had been concentrating upon the perfection of the milder-flavored tobaccos, previously prized by the industry. To furnish the manufacturers with a greater proportion of stronger-flavored tobaccos—with correspondingly higher quantities of tars and nicotine—the Department cut the price supports on several varieties of mild, bright leaf Virginia tobaccos to fifty per cent of their former levels, thereby forcing the farmer to switch to the cultivation of stronger varieties. The Division took this action heedless of the fact that the use of stronger tobaccos in filter cigarettes could serve only to render illusory the purported protection of the filter.

Many good citizens, with perhaps more sentiment than wit, have looked to Congress for leadership in developing solutions to the smoking problem. Their expectations have not been richly rewarded, even though Congress has had adequate opportunity to consider the subject of tobacco and health. The Library of Congress succeeded in unearthing for me some thirty legislative proposals designed to treat various aspects of the smoking problem which have been, at one time or another, laid before Congress.

Of course a large number of these bills bore a pure Prohibitionist stamp. Equally as many, however, were moderate, rational measures provoked solely by the medical evidence against smoking. Several bills would have provided funds for smoking education. Others would have required appropriate labeling of cigarette packages with warning signs or prominently displayed statements of tar and nicotine content.

My husband, the late Senator Richard Neuberger, was the author of two of these bills. Dick considered it a scandalous anomaly that tobacco was supported as one of America's "six basic crops," at the very time that the public health arm of the Federal Government was bearing witness to its harm. Introducing a bill to remove tobacco from the list of basic crops, he observed that many agricultural commodities that contributed not only to the nation's economy but also to its nutrition (as tobacco does not) were denied the select "basic" status. Dick also introduced a bill to provide generous grants-in-aid to support state educational programs on the hazards of smoking.

No bill relating to the smoking problem has ever been accorded even a perfunctory hearing. Each was permanently and unceremoniously interred in committee.

The chronicle of antismoking legislation's progress (or rather lack of progress) in Congress was brightened briefly by Congressman John Blatnik's Government Operations Subcommittee's 1957 investigation of false and misleading filter-tip advertising.

The Blatnik hearings remain to this day a model of legislative statesmanship. The subcommittee enlisted the testimony of many of the very scientists who had uncovered the link between smoking and disease and provided for them a forum for a forthright presentation of the medical evidence against smoking. The tactics of industry and the indifference of government were equally well illuminated. And the Committee report that followed the hearings was concise, informative, and devastating in its indictment of both industry and government.

Yet even John Blatnik's heroic efforts failed to awake Congress. The Blatnik subcommittee was abruptly dissolved by order of the Committee Chairman, Congressman William Dawson, though further hearings had already been planned and even scheduled. Moreover, the excellent Blatnik bill on cigarette advertising—the careful product of the subcommittee's hearings and deliberations—was destined for no more auspicious fate. The Blatnik bill, incidentally, included the novel and provocative suggestion that Congress set acceptable tar and nicotine levels for filter-tip cigarettes, a suggestion which certainly merited less cavalier treatment.

Yet these efforts were not wasted. The Blatnik hearings, the various bills and attendant speeches, all served to publicize the evidence against smoking. Moreover, public endorsement by legislators served to demonstrate to the public the strength and authority of that evidence.

The floor of the Senate also furnished one of the few uninhibited forums for informing the Americans of the extent to which the tobacco industry was committed to suppressing authoritative information about smoking and health. I remember that Dick unearthed a particularly odious column in an issue of the magazine *Tobacco, The International Weekly Of Industry And Science*:

> Here's something new the cigarette industry must face: New York City's Bureau of Public Health Education has completed a program to deter schoolchildren and teen-agers from smoking. Dr. Morey R. Fields, director of the bureau, says the drive will also include education on the harmful effects of narcotics and alcohol. Miss Mary Fitzgerald, associate director of health education of the board of education, said the program would seek to chiefly impress boys and girls between 11 and 13 years of age. Support will be had from the parent and teacher associations, youth organizations, city agencies with youth programs, and the tobacco industry. The topics of talks to the children, said Dr. Fields, will be informative "of the relationship between smoking and lung

cancer and cardiac involvement" and how smoking is linked
to such illnesses as Buerger's disease and gangrene.

The disturbing factor about the New York City school
antismoking educational drive is that other cities might follow. It might deter all children from ever becoming smokers.
However, for some 300 years antitobacco crusaders have
loudly predicted dire consequences for tobacco users. Yet,
despite these warnings per capita consumption has steadily
increased. The industry is currently doing its largest sales
volume in history and undoubtedly enjoying its most profitable period.

Dick took accurate aim at this witless display of cynicism:

"Today's adolescents are tomorrow's addicts," is the theme
which threads through all cigarette advertising. Yet despite
its cynical manipulation of symbols in an effort to boost sales
figures, some tobacco interests have the temerity to criticize
efforts to present another view of cigarette smoking.

One can almost picture the counterpart of these tobacco
spokesmen at the time of Pasteur's discovery of the relationship between fermentation in liquids and the growth of
bacteria, a discovery which resulted in the development of
pasteurization of milk and is today regarded as a giant forward step in the battle to better protect human health.

"The disturbing factor about Dr. Pasteur's finding is that
other people may find out," this advertising ancestor would
say, "it might deter all people from drinking raw milk."

Yet, if the pages of the Congressional Record did serve to
educate an appreciable segment of the public to the dangers
of smoking and the irresponsibility of the industry, they were
utilized with equal freedom for tobacco industry propaganda.
With unnerving regularity, tobacco states congressmen would
rise, seriatim, to denounce as subversive even the mildest
suggestion that tobacco was anything but balm to body
and soul.

More often than not, the industry was permitted to speak

for itself as a North Carolina or Virginia congressman would enshrine in the *Record* a speech by the president of a tobacco company, the current head of the Tobacco Institute, or by one of the handful of scientists friendly to the tobacco industry.

The House of Representatives, in particular, rang with ridicule of the "antitobacco fanatics" and with patriotic hymns to the economic importance of tobacco—Lord help those who failed to appreciate the social value of cigarette taxes!

I know of one tobacco state congressman who has decreed prohibition against smoking in all of his offices. I understand that he even required his staff to read and initial an essay which I circulated detailing the medical case against smoking. His position on this matter has not been widely advertised. The positions of his Congressional colleagues, however, have.

Despite the Federal Trade Commission's devotion to squeezing health claims, both overt and implied, out of cigarette ads (see Chapters 3 and 4), the Commission's reluctance to utilize its full authority to police cigarette advertising has been less than exemplary.

Writing to Chairman Paul Rand Dixon in April 1962, I expressed my conviction that any cigarette commercial or advertisement which failed to contain an adequate warning of the hazards of smoking was inherently deceptive, and I asked him if the Commission was not presently empowered to cure such deception.

The reply (after three apparently agonizing months) was mildly encouraging. The Commission acknowledged, in principle at least, its authority to require affirmative warnings to avoid deception.

If the Commission is able to secure competent probative scientific evidence including that furnished by the Public

Health Service, that a causal relationship exists between cigarette smoking and lung cancer, heart ailments, etc., it is
likely that an order of the Commission, based on such evidence, which required an affirmative disclosure of the possible hazards to health from smoking cigarettes, would be
upheld in the appellate courts.

So far, so good.

"But," continued the Commission, deftly juggling the
oranges so that I might not notice the elephant walking by,
"we have been informed by the Public Health Service that
the scientific evidence now accumulated is such as to remove
almost the last doubt that there are any health effects associated with smoking." And, since the *last doubt* had not been
removed, the Commission feared that any such order would
throw it into the courts for a "long, involved, and protracted
trial." The letter concluded, ". . . we do not believe it would
be advisable for the Commission to institute a case which
has as its objective the type of order you suggest, unless and
until there is available the required evidence."

What required evidence? Evidence which would remove
the "last doubt"? That seemed like an awfully heavy burden
for a government agency to bear in order to sustain an administrative finding, so I consulted several government at-
torneys familiar with the wilderness of administrative law.

There isn't a ghost of a suggestion in the Administrative
Procedures Act, they informed me, that would require the
Commission to prove beyond the "last doubt" that smoking
was a health hazard. All that the Commission is required to
show is that its orders are based upon "substantial evidence."
And "substantial evidence," they explained, is that evidence
upon which a reasonable man could base a conclusion that
cigarette smoking was dangerous. This is the very same burden of proof that cancer-ridden smokers suing tobacco companies are required to sustain if they are to have their cases
submitted to the jury. And in both of the last two suits by

lung-cancer victims against tobacco companies, the courts have ruled that there was sufficient evidence that smoking caused lung cancer to permit the jury to decide if the complainant was entitled to damages.

I fear that the Commission has been unduly modest in assessing its ability to succeed in a court test. Of course, I'm assuming that the Commission is more concerned with fulfilling its obligation to the public than preserving its won and lost records in the courts.

To the considerable credit of the Public Health Service, it has shown less of a tendency to avoid the smoking controversy than have its brother agencies (with the possible exception of the Federal Trade Commission) and the Congress. Yet, to describe the Service's activity in the smoking controversy as less than bold would decidedly be an understatement.

While evidence incriminating smoking was current in scientific circles as early as 1950, the Public Health Service maintained an unbroken silence on smoking until 1959. After nine years of deliberation, the statement that at last appeared in the *Journal of the American Medical Association* for November, 1959, must have fallen upon the ears of the scientific community in the words of T. S. Eliot, "Not with a bang, but a whimper." Even then, it was apparently only through the persistence of Surgeon General Leroy F. Burney that the service was moved to speak at all.

The heart of the Public Health Service position was the conclusion that: "the weight of evidence at present implicates smoking as the principal etiological factor in the increased incidence of lung cancer." This statement came more than two years later and was appreciably less succinct than the American Cancer Society's official statement that it was "beyond reasonable doubt that cigarette smoking is the major cause of the unprecedented increase in lung cancer." Moreover, the Service's statement dealt solely with lung cancer, though substantial evidence already existed of the tie between smoking and other diseases.

The appearance of the Public Health Service statement should have been the occasion for the launching of a powerful smoking education campaign, since the Public Health Service Act expressly requires the dissemination to the public of information vital to health. Instead, the Service was content primarily to furnish copies of its carefully measured prose to any interested parties. I wonder how many teenagers resisted the temptation to light up their first cigarette after reading the stirring pronouncement that smoking was *probably* the "principal etiological factor" in the increase of lung cancer.

While it is true, of course, that the Public Health Service has supported several significant research projects that have added measurably to our knowledge of the role of smoking in disease, there has been a noticeable lack of initiative and imagination in the conception of these projects. For example, the Service was content to dismiss all filters, high-filtration or low-filtration, with the terse observation that "no method of treating tobacco or filtering the smoke has been demonstrated to be effective in materially reducing or eliminating the hazard of lung cancer." Nor, for that matter, had all filters been demonstrated to be ineffective. Yet, to my knowledge, the Public Health Service has neither initiated nor supported research directed toward the development and testing of truly effective filters.

In March 1962, disheartened by the apparent lack of vigor with which the Public Health Service was fulfilling its role as guardian of the public health, I introduced in the Senate a joint resolution on tobacco and health (S. J. Res. 174). The resolution would have directed the President initially to mount a massive health-education program concerning the hazards of smoking. It also called for the formation of a Presidential Commission on Tobacco and Health, charged with the task of formulating a coherent and comprehensive program to check smoking-caused disease and to soften, if possible, any attendant hardship upon the tobacco industry. The resolution attracted the sponsorship of six of my colleagues, and though its legislative prognosis was dim, succeeded in serving notice upon the Administration that at least a handful of Senators considered the government's previous efforts in this area wholly inadequate.

The introduction of the resolution paralleled renewed public interest and concern in this country over the smoking problem, stimulated, in large part, by the publication, both in England and here, of the brilliant Royal College of Physicians' Report. Even the press was shaken from its accustomed lethargy in treating the smoking problem. Few were the newspapers and national magazines with any claim to coverage of public affairs that failed to carry at least a précis of the Royal College's conclusions. For some reason Americans always seem willing to accord more respect to nonresident oracles than their own. So it was with the Report of the Royal College.

Even if the Surgeon General's 1959 statement had represented a fair, if conservative, account of the state of medical knowledge in 1959, the evidence against smoking continued to harden during the intervening years. Clinical as well as statistical studies now seemed to exclude the possibility of error. In that same spring of 1962, Dr. Shimkin of the Cancer Institute told a conference in Phoenix that the causal relationship between smoking and cancer was now "as clearly demonstrated as any biological association can be."

The time seemed ripe for the Administration and the Surgeon General to take a more active, less equivocal role in relation to smoking.

On May 18 I wrote to the new Surgeon General, Dr. Luther Terry, asking if Dr. Shimkin's position was not now

closer to a true evaluation of the evidence against smoking
than the bland statement of his predecessor.

While I waited for an answer, the public clamor finally
reached the White House. On May 23 at his press conference
President Kennedy was asked:

Mr. President, there is another health problem that seems
to be causing growing concern here and abroad and I think
this is largely being provoked by a series of independent
scientific investigations, which have concluded that cigarette
smoking and certain types of cancer and heart disease have
a causal connection.

I have two questions. Do you and your health advisors
agree or disagree with these findings, and secondly, what if
anything should or can the Federal Government do in the
circumstances?

The President warily replied:

That matter is sensitive enough and the stock market is in
sufficient difficulty without my giving you an answer which
is not based on complete information, which I don't have
and, therefore, perhaps I would be glad to respond to that
question in more detail next week.

Five days later the *Wall Street Journal* was predicting that
the Surgeon General would convene a panel of nongovernment scientists "to assess all the health hazards of smoking
in light of the most recent evidence, and to recommend what
steps, if any, the Government should take to combat them."
The *Journal* sagely observed that the formation of such a
panel would serve "the tactical purpose of gaining time for
deliberate action and taking public pressure off Government
officials."

Three days later on June 7 at 11 A.M., the Surgeon General
released the following statement:

For a number of years the Public Health Service has supported research to determine whether smoking has any im-

pact on health. Considerable evidence has been accumulated on this subject for many years. It is timely to undertake a review of all available data. I have decided, therefore, to appoint a Committee of experts to study all evidence and make whatever recommendations are necessary. This Advisory Committee will be made up of experts from federal agencies of the government, nongovernment professional groups, health organizations and the tobacco industry. Membership will be announced when the panel is completed.

At 3:30 P.M. that same day, the President was asked:

Mr. President, can you comment on the Public Health Service announcement of a special panel of experts to study whether there is a link between cigarette smoking and certain killer diseases, and can you tell us whether the study will be a matter of months or years, or just what it is?

The President, fully armed, responded readily:

I think the statement that the Surgeon General issued this morning, I think, gives the position of the Surgeon General, which I have supported, and in response to the question which you asked two weeks ago.

Now the survey would take some months or go into 1963, but I think that the announcement is in response to your question. You have been answered.

This particular narrative ended the next day when I received a reply to my inquiry of the Surgeon General:

In reference to your letter of May 18, Dr. Burney's statement in the November 28, 1959, issue of the *Journal of the American Medical Association*, which you quote in part, is still the official position of the Public Health Service. You refer to Dr. Shimkin's statement that the causal relationship between smoking and cancer "is as clearly demonstrated as any biological association can be." To the extent that this statement is interpreted as being stronger than Dr. Burney's statement, then it is not consistent with the official PHS position.

On the other hand, we believe that the 1959 position needs to be re-examined. Sufficient new evidence seems to have accumulated to warrant this action. In addition, it should be noted that Dr. Burney's 1959 statement was concerned almost solely with smoking and lung cancer. There is also considerable evidence linking smoking with other adverse health effects. This evidence needs to be evaluated. Lastly, we feel that further study of available data is necessary to define more clearly the magnitude of any adverse health effects.

We intend to re-evaluate the points mentioned above systematically and thoroughly. We cannot predict with any certainty when the results will be available. In addition to our own staff efforts, we intend to seek the most competent and the most impartial advice and assistance that can be found. We feel this is imperative in view of the potential gravity of the problem and as a basis for any practical corrective actions which may be indicated. As you know, the Surgeon General announced on June 7 his decision to appoint an expert advisory committee to assist in these evaluations and to make whatever recommendations as may be appropriate.

We are very grateful for the constructive role you have played in these developments.

A quick-witted Government scientist promptly labeled the President's Committee the "flat earth committee." I had my own doubts. It was true that my resolution had sought the formation of a panel on smoking and health, but there were significant variations between what I had proposed and what the Surgeon General now contemplated.

One thing we did not need was one more review, from scratch, of all the previous papers and earlier reviews—as if no competent body had yet determined that cigarette smoking was a hazard. What *was* needed was a concentrated study to facilitate the translation of the medical evidence into a program of responsible action. The Surgeon General's panel was, nevertheless, going to begin at the very beginning. This unhappy fact lent some credence to the skeptical, who interpreted the Surgeon General's decision as merely one more sign of the Administration's sensitivity to both the industry and the stock market.

The birth pangs of the Surgeon General's committee were less than reassuring. The Surgeon General's original statement had indicated that the tobacco industry would be directly represented on the advisory panel—a procedure roughly akin to packing a jury with members of the accused's family. Apparently the Surgeon General had second thoughts. The committee was to be composed, rather, of scientists who had taken no public stand on the smoking issue. The tobacco industry, through the ubiquitous Tobacco Institute, was afforded a right of veto over any member of the panel—a device not without its own potential abuses.

The first name associated with the Committee was that of Dr. Herman Kraybill, a distinguished scientist in the employ of the National Cancer Institute, who was named Executive Director of the Advisory Committee prior to the selection of the members of the Committee itself. It was an auspicious appointment. Dr. Kraybill's qualifications and disinterested integrity were unassailable.

Unhappily, Dr. Kraybill soon made the unpardonable sin of admitting to a reporter from his home-town newspaper that he believed the evidence "definitely suggests that tobacco is a health hazard." This indiscretion led swiftly to Dr. Kraybill's unceremonious bouncing from his newly acquired position and to the appointment of a more circumspect successor.

Despite this unhappy assortment of ill omens, the Committee can make a genuine contribution to a governmental solution of the smoking problem. Even with the industry's veto power, which was not to my knowledge liberally exercised, the final complexion of the Committee was to all outward appearances characterized by both high qualifications and the absence of bias.

The Surgeon General, to his substantial credit, is apparently succeeding in isolating the Committee from the winds of political pressure—a task, incidentally, made immeasurably more difficult by his boss, Secretary of Health, Education and Welfare, Anthony Celebrezze, who punctuated the Committee's deliberations with the published comment that he did not consider it "the proper role of the Federal government to tell citizens to stop smoking." This curiously ambiguous statement could have meant simply that prohibition was not a solution to the smoking problem. It could equally have been interpreted as denying the government's responsibility even to educate its citizens to the dangers of smoking. The Secretary, apparently disinclined to await the outcome of the Committee's deliberations, also arbitrarily lumped smoking with "overeating, overdrinking, and other overindulgences," although the evidence, as we have seen, is that smoking is a hazard even when indulged in moderately. Whatever the Secretary's intentions, his remarks left an unfortunate mist over the Committee's deliberations and resulted, in the words of *The New York Times*, in placing "an influential official on record against strong action by the Government."

If I am less than optimistic about the deliberations of the Committee, it is because I am fearful that they may be afflicted with the same disease that struck Lincoln's generals; a disease which Lincoln himself diagnosed as "the slows." Yet I am hopeful too that the Committee's report, when finally delivered, will serve to remove the element of hedging that characterized Surgeon General Burney's 1959 statement. If it does this, it will remove the last remaining barrier to firm Administration action.

5

An
Impregnable Citadel

Since I began my campaign against the "demon tobacco," I have received many kind and generous letters from equally troubled citizens commending my efforts and, not infrequently, my "courage." I am always grateful for these letters. Goodness knows, politicians are rarely enough accused of displaying courage. And yet, to be perfectly honest, it really doesn't require very much courage for me to oppose the cigarette industry. Perseverance? Oh my, yes. But courage? Not especially.

Of course, if thousands of acres of burley tobacco, instead of wheat, grew in Eastern Oregon, or if Portland and Salem were as economically in thrall to the manufacture of cigarettes as such North Carolina cities as Durham and Winston-Salem, I might not be diffident about accepting praise for my courage.

The fact is, of course, that Oregon grows no tobacco, manufactures no cigarettes. Oddly enough, Oregon is one of only three states in the Union without a cigarette tax (though I have long argued for one) so that even the State Treasury is not threatened by my activities. I don't fear the loss of campaign contributions from the tobacco industry since I could hardly lose what I never have had. Nor am I afraid of economic or political reprisals from the tobacco industry. No doubt their public relations experts shudder at the publicity which would attend the spectacle of a multibillion-dollar industry persecuting a lone, female Senator.

(For a brief moment last April as black clouds of soot came pouring forth from the ventilators in my offices, my staff saw visions of a tobacco industry plot to blacken not only my name, but the rest of me as well. It was, alas for the lack of melodrama, just another aberration of the Senate Office Building's quaint heating and air-conditioning system.)

I am not making this disclaimer of courage because I enjoy being ungracious in rebuffing sincere compliments. But it is poor politics to credit an adversary with powers that it does not possess. It is essential that we take accurate measure of the strengths and weaknesses of the opposing parties. Tobacco men are not demons riding in the night; they possess no occult powers. And, though it would be quixotic to ignore the potent economic and political influence of tobacco, it would be equally quixotic to overestimate its strengths.

There is, of course, nothing essentially immoral in the cultivation of tobacco, nor in the manufacture and distribution of cigarettes. As Lord Taylor observed during the House of Lords debates on smoking, "There was no wickedness on the part of the manufacturers . . . it was just jolly bad luck." The emergence of the cigarette as a lethal instrumentality must fairly be considered as an economic calamity for that segment of our economy which Secretary of Commerce Luther Hodges once described as an "eight-billion-dollar industry, contributing to the support of millions of Americans and serving an estimated seventy million customers—an industry that touches the social and political life of all America."

The Earl of Arran has drawn a realistic and not unsympathetic sketch of the tobacco industry:

> We are attacking a strong and, until now, an impregnable citadel. The vested interests are vast and they are not by any means evil interests. There is, first of all, the state and by the state I do not mean any particular government. The most benevolent and humane of administrations would find itself hard put to do without the revenue that smoking brings in.* And there are the shareholders. My Lords, whatever our politics, let us not despite the shareholders. They are mostly small people and they rightly put their money where they think it will bring in the most. A heavy drop in the value of tobacco shares would hit them hard.†
>
> Last of all but very far from least, there are the employees— the people who work in the industry.‡ What would happen to them if cigarette smoking were suddenly to become forbidden or to become taboo? Would they overnight find new jobs? Are they to be victimized by something which is not their fault? No, my Lords, it's not so easy.

And, in America, there is the tobacco farmer. Nearly three million Americans work the nation's more than 500,000 tobacco farms. They are small farms—the average tobacco farmer plants only slightly more than 2 acres to tobacco. Yet the total yield of these farms in 1962 was over 2.2 billion pounds, valued at more than 1.3 billion dollars. Farmers in the state of North Carolina alone received 527 million dollars for their tobacco in 1961.

Moreover, the economic impact of the cigarette extends to many related industries. Most significant, certainly, in terms

* In the United States, the combined total of federal, state and municipal excise taxes on tobacco in 1962 exceeded three billion dollars. The entire state education structure in the state of South Carolina is supported solely by tobacco tax receipts.

† There are 350,000 cigarette company shareholders in this country.

‡ The Tobacco Institute estimates that the labor force engaged in this country in marketing, processing, storing, and manufacturing tobacco "is well over three million."

of tobacco's power to influence public opinion, is the industry's economic impact upon both advertising and communications. Stoic indeed is the advertising agency or publisher who operates without at least a glance over his shoulder at the 170-million-dollar annual cigarette advertising budget. As for other affected enterprises, the Tobacco Institute estimates that more than 1.5 million businesses share in the tobacco trade as suppliers of construction, equipment, materials, transportation services, and as distributors and merchandisers. The figure may be liberal, but at least it is suggestive. A good indication of the broad reach of the cigarette dollar can be seen in the surprising fact that tobacco manufacturers utilize for flavoring at least 95 per cent of all the licorice consumed in this country.

At stake, then, in the smoking controversy are dividends, profits, wages, and farm income for millions of Americans. Yet, I am not convinced that the industry opposition to anti-smoking agitation (or rather "anti-cancer" agitation) is motivated solely by cynical concern for the pocketbook. The tobacco industry is centralized. It dominates not only the economic and political scene, but also the social life of North Carolina, Kentucky, and, to a lesser extent, Virginia, South Carolina, Georgia, and Tennessee. The aroma of tobacco in the process of manufacture permeates the very air of such cities as Durham, Richmond, and Winston-Salem. To many people in these areas tobacco has become the focal point of a traditional way of life.

As a legislator I need no lessons in the powers of rationalization. It is natural for men whose lives have been devoted to the growing, processing, or the manufacture of tobacco products to seize eagerly upon the dissenting verdict of the handful of scientists who continue to dispute the findings of the majority, or to convince themselves that the furor over smoking and lung cancer reflects only the reappearance of misguided prohibitionism.

Strangely enough, the Russian experiences with the smoking problem tend to prove my point that more than money is at stake in tobacco's defense. A Soviet Embassy official here told me that Russian medical agencies are presently engaged in a heated battle with tobacco trade groups to discourage smoking. The absence of a profit motive has apparently not dimmed the ardor of the trade group's intransigence.

Of course, whether tobacco men be misguided saints or charlatans, they are united in their determination not to preside at the dissolution of their industry. To this end they are prepared to utilize every economic and political weapon at their disposal. And these weapons do form an imposing arsenal.

Quite aside from its purely economic impact, the tobacco industry enjoys a unique political position which other industries of comparable economic significance (with the possible exception of textiles and oil) do not share. As we have seen, the industry is centered in six Southern states—states which share in the disproportionate power which the one-party South and the seniority system have combined to give Southern legislators. Virginia's Senators are chairmen of the powerful Finance and Banking and Currency Committees, as well as of the Joint Committees on Reduction of Non-essential Federal Expenditures and Defense Production. Senator Olin Johnston of South Carolina chairs the Senate Post Office and Civil Service Committee; Senator Richard Russell of Georgia, the potent Armed Services Committee. Senators from tobacco states thus chair one-fourth of the Senate committees and one-half of the Joint Committees.

In the House the story is much the same. Of twenty-one committees, Congressmen from tobacco states chair seven, including the omnipotent Rules Committee. North Carolina Congressmen alone chair the House Agriculture and Merchant Marine Committees and powerful subcommittees of the Foreign Affairs and Government Operations Committees.

To this geographically derived power must be added the industry's skill and liberality in lobbying. So notoriously generous are the representatives of the cigarette companies on the state as well as the federal level that one occasionally hears of unscrupulous state legislators introducing a cigarette-labeling bill with the not unreasonable expectation of "shaking down" tobacco lobbyists for substantial "contributions" in exchange for prompt burial of the bill. (Of course, there have been perfectly legitimate and well-motivated bills of this type introduced in state legislatures throughout the country.)

The impressive economic and political potency of the tobacco industry cannot alone explain its unqualified success in staving off the forces of change. Substantial, if less visible, support for the industry continues to come from an appreciable segment of the nation's 70 million smokers, who at best are half-hearted and grudging in acknowledgment of the hazards of smoking and at their worst are blinded by their real (or felt) need for tobacco. Too often this has meant that parents, teachers, doctors, and even public officials are incapable of fulfilling their proper role in the dissemination of material about smoking or the implementation of programs to discourage smoking.

How often will a high school teacher drone through the prescribed format for smoking education, straining to complete her chores so that she can seize a five- or ten-minute smoking break in the teachers' lounge? And how often is a doctor so wedded to his own smoking habit that he is unable to lay his cigarette aside even while prescribing abstinence to his own patients. And a father's stern strictures to his son can have little currency when set in the backdrop of the father's own addiction.

Can a director of public health for a city—who is a smoker —or a Congressman faced with antismoking legislation—who is a smoker—disassociate himself from the tenacity and pleasure of his own smoking habit? It is possible, but it is not likely. Research scientists and public health officials engaged in cancer prevention relate incident after incident of antismoking plans or programs going awry because of the intransigence of a key official who happened also to be a smoker.

Who would rely on a narcotics addict to evaluate the hazards of narcotic addiction? Yet the vigor of the Administration's response to the smoking problem may lie chiefly in the hands of a confirmed pack-a-day smoker, Secretary of Health, Education and Welfare Celebrezze, who has thus far indicated that he believes the government should do little, if anything, about smoking.

With this fearful arsenal of weapons at its call, the cigarette industry would appear to have every reason to face the future with equanimity. There is, however, little joy in tobaccoland today. The tobacco man has lived and thrived under a medical cloud for 13 years, but he has not learned to like it. Unnerved in 1953-54 when cigarette sales plummeted, his spirits revived in 1955 and the years following when cigarette sales resumed their upward and outward curve. At times he could almost bring himself to believe that the "cancer scare," like James I's *Counter-Blaste to Tobacco*, would recede quietly into history. Today, however, he knows better.

This anxiety has been reflected in the stock market. Since investment capital is notoriously unsentimental, last year's disaffection of investors for cigarette company shares was surely an uneasy vote of "no confidence" in the future of the cigarette. In July 1962, Bache & Company, investment brokers, predicted that fortune would soon smile on American Tobacco, P. Lorillard, *et al.* September saw Bache less sanguine about tobacco's immediate prospects; by December, the brokerage firm had become grim about the future of the whole cigarette industry. In May 1962, cigarette share prices kept pace with the market in dropping 40 to 50 per cent. Unlike other shares, however, several of them have remained depressed.

That management is equally queasy can be seen in the current rage to diversify. Reynolds has gone into the fruit juice business in the not-unreasonable hope that canned Hawaiian Punch will prove more benign than Camels.

There was unconscious irony in two *New York Times'* accounts, published nearly a year apart almost to the day, of annual reports by President Joseph F. Cullman III to the stockholders of Philip Morris. The first article, dated April 11, 1962, carried the following ingenuous headline:

CIGARETTE THREAT CALLED UNPROVEN
Philip Morris Says Smoking Has Psychological Value

Buried at the bottom of this tale of unrestrained optimism was a brief paragraph disclosing that PM, hell-bent for diversification, had moved to increase the earnings of two major subsidiaries, Milprint Inc. and the American Safety Razor Products Corporation.

The second article on April 10, 1963 was heralded:

CANCER-LINK EXONERATION SEEN BY
PHILIP MORRIS HEAD

After the reporter had finished noting Mr. Cullman's ritualistic disclaimer, "There is increasing evidence that implicates factors other than smoking," this description of the company's drive to hedge against the future of the cigarette followed:

> Mr. Cullman also told shareholders that its subsidiary, American Safety Razor, recently had introduced its Personna Stainless Steel Double Edge Blades in New York and New England. He also expressed optimism for the Burma-Vita Company, makers of Burma Shave and other shaving products acquired in the 1963 first quarter. He said that their

products fitted well into American Safety Razor's product line-up.

Philip Morris has also reached agreement for the acquisition of the Clark Brothers Chewing Gum Company of Pittsburgh, Pennsylvania, whose principal product is Clark's Teaberry Gum, the executive disclosed. . . .

PM would like to be ready when its customers "call for" Teaberry instead of Philip Morris.

Dissension is another telltale index of fear. And there are signs of dissension in the previously monolithic unity of the tobacco industry. The Tobacco Institute may claim to voice the gospel according to 99 per cent of the industry but it is becoming increasingly plain that the Institute speaks primarily for its major benefactors, American and Reynolds.

American and Reynolds are, both commercially and emotionally, committed to the marketing of nonfilter and low-filtration cigarettes. Reynolds derives the lion's share of its profits from its sales of Camel, the leading nonfilter cigarette, and of low-filtration Winston and Salem, while 90 per cent of American's sales are of the nonfilter Pall Mall and Lucky Strike. Reflecting the interests of American and Reynolds, the Tobacco Institute treats filters as a fashion fad, a mental aberration of the smoking public. Since the Institute does not accept the evidence that smoking is harmful, it cannot conceive of any valid health function which a filter could serve. That is its posture, calculated to sell more nonfilter cigarettes than filter-tips.

P. Lorillard, however, the third-ranking cigarette maker, with 95 per cent of its sales in filter-tips, is committed to the necessity and efficacy of high-filtration filters. So are Liggett & Myers and Philip Morris. No matter how circumscribed these companies' public utterances, the fact remains that they cannot promote filters unless they are willing to concede, either expressly or by implication, that there are substances in tobacco smoke which require filtering, or, putting it another way, that unfiltered smoke is hazardous.

This intra-industry conflict has enjoyed little publicity, yet there is hard evidence of it. There was little enough show of fraternity in the wildly competitive excesses of the tar derby. The most striking display of discord, however, took place when both Lorillard and Liggett & Myers decided to make individual presentations of scientific evidence (clearly filter-oriented) to the Surgeon General's Advisory Committee.

These decisions were implemented in the face of a Tobacco Institute plea for a solid front, with the Institute as sole spokesman for the industry.

Today the industry generally retains an outward show of unanimity. There is every reason, however, to believe that the inner conflict festers as the medical evidence continues to undercut the Tobacco Institute's underpinnings, and as anxiety over the future of the cigarette deepens.

This then is the tobacco industry, a trembling Goliath. But where is the David with either the inclination or courage to fell this Goliath? Surely, the bleak record of defaulted public responsibility gives little evidence of any potent counterforce to the tobacco industry.

To begin with, there are the courts. As any Mississippian can tell you, the political power of the South is not necessarily sufficient to inure Southern interests from adverse decisions by United States Courts. And, though our courts are rarely on the frontier of social and economic reform, judicial decisions do eventually reflect progress in our society's concepts of right and responsibility—often in the face of vested interest and political pressure.

Thus, over the last half-century, American courts have tended with increasing frequency to hold the makers and distributors of products liable for harm resulting from the use of their products. Forty years ago if the wheel fell off your new car, you had no recourse against the manufacturer. Today, you do. If a shampoo caused your hair to fall out, or an adulterated soft drink made you ill, you were not likely to obtain legal redress for your injury. Today, you may recover money damages from the manufacturer of the hair product or the soft drink.

As of this date no lung-cancer victim has recovered a judgment against a cigarette company. Several have tried. The remarkable personal injury lawyer, Melvin Belli, who for good or evil has been almost singly responsible for the spectacular rise in successful medical malpractice suits, claims that cigarette companies are liable to their less fortunate customers under any of four supportable legal theories:

1. Negligence in selling, advertising, and distributing their cigarettes without warning of their dangers.
2. Negligence in giving assurances of safety in selling, advertising, and distributing their cigarettes.
3. Negligence in manufacturing, processing, mixing, and using the ingredients and tobaccos which were used.
4. Breach of implied warranties of wholesomeness.

The early cases, however, were thrown out of court by judges who decided that there was insufficient evidence of a causal relationship between smoking and lung cancer to permit the jury even to consider whether the claimant was entitled to damages.

In the most recent case of note, however, *Pritchard* vs. *Liggett & Myers* (makers of Chesterfields), the Third United States Circuit Court of Appeals, reflecting the inexorable trend toward manufacturer liability, held (1) that there was now sufficient evidence of smoking's causal role in lung cancer and (2) that the jury should be afforded the opportunity to decide whether Pritchard, who had smoked twenty to thirty Chesterfields a day for thirty years, should recover damages from Liggett & Myers. Judge Staley, speaking for the court, wrote:

. . . One who supplies a product to another and knows or should know that the foreseeable use is dangerous to human life unless certain precautions are taken, and who realizes or should realize that the user will not in the exercise of reasonable vigilance recognize the danger, is under a duty to warn the user of such consequences and to advise proper precautions. . . . The precautions necessary to comply with the standard of reasonableness vary with the danger involved. . . .

. . . one supplying a chattel is subject to liability if by word or deed he leads those who are to use the chattel to believe it to be of a character or in a condition safer for use than he knows it to be or to be likely to be.

The jury refused to award Pritchard damages, although they found as a fact that the smoking of Chesterfields had caused Pritchard's lung cancer. The jury indicated that they believed that Pritchard had taken his life in his own hands when he chose to continue smoking Chesterfields despite published reports of the harm of smoking.

The significance of the Pritchard case to the personal injury lawyer did not lie in the unfavorable jury verdict, but in the fact that the case had been submitted to the jury. "Getting to the jury" is more than half the battle for the claimant's lawyer. In the Pritchard case the jury was unsympathetic. Next time the jury may be persuaded that the company's refusal to admit the strength of the evidence against smoking, or the company's glorification of smoking in its advertising, or its attempts to discredit scientists who have condemned smoking, should render it responsible for the effects of smoking. Next time the jury may be swayed by sympathy for the client or the client's wife, or by annoyance at the company's witnesses, or even the company's "corporate image." In the Pritchard case, the jury was not so moved. Next time, who knows? In any event the tobacco industry heard, in the Pritchard opinion, one shoe fall. It is now waiting for the other to drop.*

There is no unitary political force dedicated to the control of smoking-caused diseases, but the peculiarly American genius for voluntary association and the individual American's capacity for indignation and sense of individual responsibility have combined to form a powerful, if often ragged, opposition to the tobacco industry.

Nowhere was the peculiar strength of this opposition so dramatically displayed as at a meeting held at Harrisburg, Pennsylvania, in January of 1963. Representatives of such leading voluntary associations as the American Cancer Society, the Girl Scouts of America, the Pennsylvania Medical Society, the Pennsylvania Health Association, the Pennsylvania Tuberculosis and Health Society and the Harrisburg Jewish Community Center met with state officials to examine the problem of smoking among the state's teen-age population. From this meeting emerged a vigorous, permanent program of smoking education, presently in force throughout the Pennsylvania school system.

Nor was the Pennsylvania experience unique. At the close of 1962, the American Cancer Society's superb smoking education materials had reached the pupils of 22,000 of the nation's 30,000 secondary schools. Many states and countless individual cities, backed and prodded by the voluntary associations, have displayed imagination and initiative in supplementing these materials. Maine has developed a program to appeal to the particular needs of rural teen-agers. Minnesota shows a suitable filmstrip on smoking to the preteen-age sixth- and seventh-graders. Among the nation's cities, New York

* The shoe may this very moment be dropping in the case of Green vs. American Tobacco Company, in which the Florida Supreme Court has advised that the law of Florida does "impose on a manufacturer and distributor of cigarettes absolute liability . . . for death caused by using such cigarettes."

has initiated a program of in-service television training to
insure that the city's health-education teachers utilize the instruction materials effectively. Jacksonville, Florida, has enlisted the services of a panel of nonsmoking doctors, willing
to lend the authority of their profession to lectures on the
hazards of smoking.

Even in states such as North Carolina, in which resistance
to antismoking education might well have been anticipated,
the Cancer Society office reports brisk business supplying
educational materials upon request to local school boards.

To the influence of the voluntary associations must be
added the voice of that segment of the free press which has
proved free of the gag of the cigarette advertising dollar.

For more than a decade the *Reader's Digest,* scorning cigarette advertising, has reported to its substantial readership
the full measure of scientific knowledge of smoking, as well
as the failure of government and industry to mount an effective response. *Consumer's Union* has given smoking equally
responsible and exhaustive coverage. In recent years, *Time,*
Newsweek, The Atlantic Monthly, Harper's, The New
Republic, and *The Nation* have each made significant
contributions to the public dialogue about smoking, while
displaying minimal advertiser bias. Some newspapers have
followed suit.

In September 1962 Columbia Broadcasting System delivered a remarkably perceptive and objective review of the
smoking controversy, "A Study of Teen-age Smoking," to
the accompaniment of anguished howls from the Tobacco
Institute (understandably outraged at this blow from television, its erstwhile constant ally).

Church and temperance presses continue to mount effective campaigns of smoking education, coupled with appeals
to public action. I am particularly mindful of the authorita-

tives series of pamphlets titled *Smoke Signals,* widely distributed by the Seventh Day Adventists.

Magazines responding to the interests of individual citizens concerned with the nation's health, such as *Prevention* magazine have also focused attention upon the smoking problem and galvanized support for appropriate government action.

For the nation's press as a whole, it is little and it is late, but it is progress.

There are also signs that both the medical profession and its leaders are rapidly awakening to their responsibilities for smoking education. Doctors have become increasingly sensitive to criticism such as that leveled by Dr. Howard C. Taylor of Columbia University, who told his colleagues, "Doctors have no right to claim a layman's privilege of ignorance on the question of cigarette smoking and cancer. The scientist searching for the absolute truth may be justified in seeking the removal of the last shred of doubt. But the practicing physician has a responsibility to act *now* on the basis of the evidence before him. Where that evidence is compelling, as with smoking, he fails to discharge his obligation if he refuses to act." That this criticism is indeed taking hold is, I think, sharply demonstrated by a 1959 study of Massachusetts doctors that revealed that the percentage of cigarette-smoking doctors had declined since 1954 from 51.8 to 38.5. As of the time of this writing, at least eight state medical societies have passed resolutions on smoking and health: Rhode Island, Vermont, California, Georgia, Maine, New York, Pennsylvania, and Utah.

On the national level, the American Medical Association long maintained an uncharacteristic silence about smoking. As late as December 1961, Dr. I. S. Ravdin, now President of the American Cancer Society, flatly accused the A.M.A. of "pussyfooting" in its approach to smoking. Yet the A.M.A.'s unique role as spokesman on public health matters for a substantial segment of the nation's doctors made it imperative that the A.M.A. speak out on smoking.

In April 1962, I wrote to Dr. Leonard W. Larson, then President of the A.M.A., calling to his attention the long and distinguished list of public health and medical associations, both here and abroad, that had taken a position on smoking. I urged the A.M.A. to do likewise.

I received a courteous but disquieting reply. I was told that the trustees of the A.M.A. had twice in the past requested the A.M.A.'s Council on Drugs to explore the feasibility of a study on smoking, and that the Council, on both occasions, had opposed such a study. The last such refusal had been voiced just three months previously. Nevertheless, my request was to be referred to the Board of Trustees at their annual meeting the following month so that they might have the opportunity to reconsider the matter.

To be perfectly frank, I assumed that my plea would be afforded a perfunctory hearing and a brisk tabling, and that the vigorous disinclination of the Council on Drugs to embroil itself in the smoking controversy would doubtless prevail.

On June 8 I received the following short, but nonetheless satisfying, letter from Ernest B. Howard, M.D., Assistant Executive Vice President of the A.M.A.:

> The Board of Trustees of the American Medical Association considered your inquiry regarding the official position of the American Medical Association on the subject of smoking and health. I am happy to report to you that the Board instructed the Council on Drugs of the A.M.A. to study and report on the relationship of tobacco and disease. I shall keep you apprised of the progress of the Council in its study of this important subject.
>
> May I take this opportunity to congratulate you on the impetus you have given both the American Medical Associ-

ation and the Public Health Service on this important matter.

This time the Council on Drugs was not to be permitted the luxury of declining. Or so it seemed, for 9 months later I was startled and dismayed by the following headline in the *Wall Street Journal:*
"A.M.A. CANCELS STUDY OF TOBACCO'S POSSIBLE LINKS WITH DISEASES." The *Journal* reported that the Council on Drugs had been forced to drop its investigation because it was unable to enlist a sufficient number of "appropriate" scientists and physicians to conduct it.

I could well appreciate that good men who were not already convinced that smoking is a cause of disease were hard to find. Besides, the few who had remained, at least publicly, uncommitted had already been tapped by the Surgeon General to serve on his committee. Still, the decision to abandon the study could have been interpreted as a retreat by the A.M.A. from its decision of the past summer. And so the stock market chose to interpret it, as prices of cigarette shares bounded buoyantly upward on each of the three days succeeding the A.M.A. announcement.

I am now satisfied that both my initial distress and the ebulliency of the stock market were premature. The critical test of A.M.A. good faith lies not in its readiness to undertake yet another review of the scientific data, but in its willingness to take an official stand on smoking and health. Subsequent statements by A.M.A. spokesmen make it quite clear that the primary reason for cancelling the study was the pendency of the report by the Surgeon General's Committee. "Since Surgeon General Luther Terry has appointed a Committee of outstanding scientists to continue such a study," said A.M.A. Vice President F. J. L. Blasingame, "the A.M.A.'s Council felt that there should not be duplication of effort."

Dr. Blasingame reaffirmed the Board of Trustees commitment to adopt an official position on smoking: "The A.M.A. has been assured early access to the report of the Surgeon General's Advisory Committee. After a study of the report, the A.M.A. *will* make a statement based on a critical evaluation of the data." (My italics.)

Hopefully, this A.M.A. action will serve to remove the last vestige of respectability in the industry-nurtured notion that there remains any serious doubt of the harmful effects of smoking. It should complement and reinforce the Surgeon General's own statements and, as the voice of the doctors' own organization, will undoubtedly make manifest to the individual doctor his peculiar responsibility in inhibiting smoking.

I would hardly presume to call the role of public figures who have risen to provide leadership in countering the efforts of the cigarette industry. Yet I am convinced that these individual acts of leadership will weigh heavily in the eventual balances struck with the cigarette industry. When LeRoy Collins, heedless of commercial interest or pressure, condemns the moral irresponsibility of the industry and its communications handmaidens, his words reverberate throughout the country. And a Congressman or commentator with the force and integrity of John Blatnik or Edward P. Morgan can evoke a response from the American public.

No post or profession enjoys a monopoly of inspired leadership. There have been leaders among practicing physicians: Drs. Alton Ochsner and Richard N. Overholt, lung surgeons whose daily contact with the anguish of smokers stricken with lung cancer has provoked them to speak out on the dangers of smoking. There have been research scientists, such as Hammond, Horn, Shimkin and Wynder, who have reluctantly taken leave of their laboratories and offices to disseminate their findings to the public, regardless of the abuse and personal disaparagement that has been the industry's reward for their efforts.

And from the medical schools have come articulate voices challenging Americans to accept the clear evidence of the scientists and to get on with the business of doing something about it. Men such as Dr. David Rutstein of Harvard have publicly stripped the cover of reasonableness from the industry's specious protestations.

I doubt if any individual act of leadership succeeded in unnerving the tobacco industry as completely as the October 1962 decision by the Air Force Surgeon General, Major General Oliver K. Niess, to terminate distribution of free cigarettes in Air Force hospitals and clinics and in flight lunches.

This was in many ways a remarkable decision. When the Surgeon General of the Public Health Service had announced his plans for the formation of the Advisory Committee in June 1962, I, for one, despaired of stimulating any further government action until the Advisory Committee had spoken. Surely government officials who had already demonstrated their distaste for tackling the smoking problem would welcome the pendancy of the report as a perfect excuse for sitting on their hands.

This gloomy prognosis, however, failed to account for the integrity and tenacity of the Air Force Surgeon General. His action was a lonely one. It was taken, so far as I can tell, with no visible political support. It was, moreover, an action that was bound to be singularly unpopular. (As one cigarette company official exclaimed in disbelief, "I have never heard of anyone turning down free cigarettes. For thirty years the Services have been trying to get all the free cigarettes they could.")

But if it was a hard decision, it was also exactly right. As the Deputy Air Force Surgeon General observed in the memorandum explaining the action, "To allow the free distribution of cigarettes in our hospitals and our flight lunches suggests to our personnel that the Air Force, in effect, condones cigarette smoking. To do so is to repudiate the overwhelming evidence of many medical research teams working independently on a world-wide basis."

One aspect of the Air Force action deserves particular attention. In informing the cigarette companies of his decision, the Surgeon General made a standing offer to reconsider his position whenever the cigarette companies were able to present competent medical evidence disproving the causal connection between smoking and disease. Again, this was exactly right.

Smoking has been found guilty, not of a few minor misdemeanors but of decimating the smoking population. Medical authorities should no longer bear the burden of eliminating every industry quibble or scintilla of doubt. Where there remains so little doubt, the cigarette industry should not be given the benefit of it.

To the tobacco industry, the chilling message of Surgeon General Niess' action was that a responsible official, acting upon sound medical testimony, was beyond the reach of all the economic power, of all the political pressure, that the industry could muster.

6

Safe Cigarettes?

Within the confines of a vast cigarette company laboratory in North Carolina, a half-dozen white-frocked chemists and lab assistants tend curious complexes of metal and glass known simply and accurately as "smoking machines."

In several rooms there are smoking machines precisely designed to enable the chemists to simulate the smoking patterns of the human smoker. An intricate timing mechanism determines the interval and length of each puff the machine draws. Here are compared the quantities of tar and nicotine which will be produced by given cigarettes when smoked by the average smoker. As one watches the smoldering cigarettes jutting out from their metal receptacles, periodically aglow, it is as if some disembodied lung were rhythmically inhaling long, deep draughts of smoke.

Beneath the laboratory, in a large, hot basement room labeled whimsically "the tar factory," stands a grosser smoking machine with great black spokes emerging from a central core, each spoke holding and consuming as many as fifty cigarettes simultaneously. The smoke is sucked into the central core and drawn over dry ice, condensing to produce jar after jar of blackish, viscous tar. One of the two men whose sole task is to supply these insatiable machines with cigarettes looks up smiling, "If we really want to get a lot of tar in a hurry, we feed it Brand X's" (competitor's notoriously strong cigarette).

The production of tar is the first step in a laborious chain of steps that has as its ultimate goal the isolation and identification of each of the constituent components of tobacco tar.

As the tar is separated or "fractionated" by successive refining procedures the chemist must employ the most advanced techniques of his profession, the measurement of radiation and of infrared and ultraviolet images, to identify components of the tar that may constitute as minute a fraction as one-millionth or even one-billionth part.

How close are they to achieving their goal? A young chemist in charge answers: "We have already succeeded in identifying between five and six hundred distinct chemical components in tar." What percentage of the total components does this represent? The young chemist shrugs, "Probably no more than 25 per cent."

The dream of the men in this laboratory, and undoubtedly of men in similar cigarette company laboratories elsewhere, is of a perfect filter that will extract from the smoke each chemical component or group of components identified by the laboratories as carcinogenic or otherwise undesirable, and will pass through to the smoker only those components that, recognized as sources of tobacco's unique taste and flavor, have, in addition, been proved safe. The realization of this dream would undoubtedly save the lives of hundreds of thousands of Americans, it would preserve an eight-billion-dollar industry, and it would bring vast fortunes to all who participated in its realization. Nevertheless, the realization of this dream is both problematical and distant.

The Director of Research tells fondly of having isolated a

tiny fraction of tar so aromatic and delectable that a few drops of it engulf a room in the most exquisite fragrance. He tells of other components emitting the putrid odor of rotten fish. How perfect it would be if the noxious substance were the only source of disease in smoke and the fragrant fraction free from suspicion!

To date there is sparse evidence that it will ever be possible to separate flavor from hazard in smoke. Dr. Ernest Wynder of the Sloan-Kettering Institute, an expert witness to the hazards of smoking, and a scientist with a fair claim to the title of "Filter Expert," recently suggested that a newly marketed filter additive was capable of selectively removing a significant segment of the phenols in smoke. (The phenols, as we have seen, are among the most suspect co-carcinogenic components of smoke.) Moreover, this additive apparently passed sufficient quantities of the remaining components of the smoke to give the smoker a satisfactory taste and flavor.

But this is little more than a promising start. Phenols are by no means the only known co-carcinogenic agent in smoke. Dr. Wynder, himself, has warned that the filter manufacturer cannot ignore the apparent relationship of nicotine to cardiovascular disease. There is some evidence that smokers are unsatisfied by low nicotine cigarettes, that the stimulation of nicotine furnishes a significant element of the pleasure of smoking. (See Chapter 7.)

Nor is there any assurance that the high flavor-bearing components of the smoke will not also be revealed as carcinogenic. Moreover, smoking has varied deleterious effects on health: cancer, heart disease, emphysema, peptic ulcers, and so forth; each may be affected by distinct components of the smoke.

For the present and the foreseeable future, selective filtration is still largely a dream. This is not to suggest, however, that cigarette manufacturers are today incapable of producing filters that can substantially, though nonselectively, reduce the incriminated agents in smoke.

Several months ago I received a letter from a Wisconsin man who claimed to have developed a perfect filter—a filter whose efficiency could be varied to remove any proportion of the cigarette's tar and nicotine that the maker desired. And what was the substance that could filter so miraculously? Cheese—Wisconsin cheese.

It seemed to me that any man who offered a promise, however unlikely, of solving not only the smoking problem but the nagging headache of dairy surpluses to boot, deserved more than token consideration. I showed his letter to Dr. Michael Shimkin at the National Cancer Institute and asked for his comments. Dr. Shimkin's reply was brief and to the point, "It's a marvelous idea," he said, "if you happen to like cheese."

He explained that there were any number of substances which could be employed effectively to filter the passage of tar and nicotine, but these substances, including cellulose acetate, which is utilized in the majority of filters presently marketed, are nonselective. That is, they filter a given proportion of the tar and nicotine without differentiating between hazardous components and flavor components. Thus, the safer the cigarette, the less palatable.

In 1952 the P. Lorillard Company introduced Kent, the first cigarette with a relatively efficient filter, a filter that subjected the Kent smoker to approximately 50 per cent less tar and nicotine than the average contemporary, nonfilter cigarette. Liggett & Myers followed with its filtered L&M, producing significantly less tar and nicotine than average nonfilter cigarettes, though not quite as efficient as the first Kent.

There is little doubt that smokers who switched to these cigarettes received a substantial benefit. Dr. Hammond, for example, noted the absence of the significant symptoms of coughing and shortness of breath among the smokers of high-filtration cigarettes. The experiments of a research team at Buffalo's Roswell Park Memorial Institute reinforced these findings. Extracting tar from four brands of unfiltered and two brands of filtered cigarettes to apply to the skin of laboratory mice, the Roswell Park doctors found that the filtered cigarettes produced a third less tar and that these reduced quantities of tar produced significantly fewer skin tumors upon laboratory mice than the greater quantities of tar produced by the nonfilter cigarettes.

Dr. Wynder, testifying before the Blatnik Committee, reached the same conclusion:

> It is feasible to produce filter tips with a satisfactory pressure drop and satisfactory flavor which can remove about 40 per cent of the tar of the cigarette smoke. Such a filter incorporated in a regular-size cigarette, which normally yields 30 milligrams of tar in its smoke, can reduce the tar exposure of a given individual smoking this cigarette to about 18 milligrams. A reduction to such level, as animal experiments as well as the human statistical studies show, will be followed by a significant reduction in cancer risk, provided, of course, that the number of cigarettes smoked is kept constant.

The ultimate value of filters has long been clouded, however, by a statement made by former FTC chairman John Gwynne to the Blatnik Committee in July, 1958:

> We have completed a consumer survey conducted for the purpose of determining primarily what results smokers expect from smoking filter-tip cigarettes. In the course of the survey, the Commission's Bureau of Investigation interviewed smokers of filter-tip cigarettes in widely scattered areas of the country who smoke over 10 cigarettes a day. . . .
> . . . As to the comparative number of cigarettes smoked a day, more than half said they smoked the same number

while approximately 30 per cent said they smoked more filter-tips.

To this statement can be traced the widely held popular belief that the filter-tip convert simply expands his consumption of filters until he succeeds in exposing himself to the same quantities of tar and nicotine as before. And it is this belief, I am convinced, that explains the relative lack of interest among public health officials in looking to effective filtration as part of the solution to the smoking problem.

How conclusive was this highly significant FTC survey? For 5 years no one outside of the FTC was in a position to judge, for the methodology and data of the survey were classified confidential by the Commission and shielded from public scrutiny until April of this year. At that time, following my request to Chairman Paul Rand Dixon, the survey files were opened for inspection to a member of my staff and a psychologist with broad experience in the field of smoking behavior.

The survey, upon analysis, fails to support the proposition that the nonfilter smoker who switches to a filter-tip brand is likely to smoke more. Studies of smoking behavior by Dr. Horn and others have indicated both that filter-tip smokers tend to be bunched in lower age groups and that *all* smokers tend gradually to increase their consumption of cigarettes until the age of 35 or 40 years. Thus, in all probability, the FTC would also have discovered some increased consumption among nonfilter smokers with the same age characteristics as the 360 filter smokers actually polled. Moreover, the FTC sample excluded filter-tip smokers who, at the time of the survey, smoked less than ten cigarettes a day, thereby eliminating an undetermined number of smokers who previously had smoked more than ten nonfilter cigarettes a day but, after switching to filters, had decreased their consumption to below ten cigarettes a day. Finally, though Chairman Gwynne was generous with the intelligence that 30 per cent of the filter-tip smokers said that they smoked more, he failed to add that 11 per cent had said that they smoked less.

Taking each of these flaws into account, we concluded that the survey yields no conclusive evidence one way or another as to the effects upon cigarette consumption of switching from nonfilters to filters. As a matter of fact, the researchers I have talked to believe that the evidence points in the other direction—that the filter-tip smoker may very well tend to cut down on his over-all consumption. The present Commission now takes no official position on the significance of its survey, although it is apparent that the findings influenced the earlier FTC decision to press for the elimination of tar and nicotine claims from cigarette advertising.

The commercial success of the first filter-tip cigarette was nothing short of phenomenal. In 1952, only 1.5 per cent of the cigarettes sold in this country had filters. By 1956, filter-tip sales had ballooned to 30 per cent of the market. Today, sales of filter-tip cigarettes account for 56 per cent of all cigarette sales, and the president of one cigarette company recently predicted that the filter-tip cigarette will eventually occupy 75 per cent of the cigarette market.

It is absolutely clear that the catalyst affecting the growth of filter sales was the appearance in 1954 of the startling Hammond and Horn report and its ensuing publicity, particularly in the *Reader's Digest*. Smokers, deeply moved by the evidence against smoking, turned to the filter to allay their fears while preserving the pleasure or addiction of their habit. And, instead of entering into a slow and fateful decline, over-all cigarette consumption, after a brief respite, resumed its historic rise.

Several of the major manufacturers saw in the filter their salvation and shifted a heavy segment of their capital, and their advertising toward effecting the great switch from nonfilters to filters—to Kent, "with the Micronite filter" that "takes out more nicotine and tars than any other leading cigarette—the difference in protection is priceless"; to L&M, upon the faith that "no filter compares with L&M's miracle tip—more flavor, less nicotine"; to Winston, which "filters so effectively"; to others, that promised "more effective filtration"; and to still others, that guaranteed "cleaner, milder, safer smoking."

But once the smoker determined to seek safety in filters, upon what basis was he to choose his brand? He found no guideposts to direct him to the most effective filters. Cigarette ads were his principal source of information (although more circumspect smokers followed the tar and nicotine ratings in the *Reader's Digest* or *Consumer Reports*). And when the smoker surveyed the ads with their wildly conflicting claims he became, in the words of a January 24, 1958, *Wall Street Journal* article, "utterly confused":

> And there's little chance that the confusion will end any time soon. Take a look at cigarette advertising, which offers a maze of figures to the consumer. A couple of ads carry graphs showing milligrams of tars and nicotine in various brands. (The brand doing the advertising naturally comes out best in its own graph.) Philip Morris says its new Parliament filter has "30,000 filaments." Liggett & Myers Tobacco Company's television commercials talk about its L&M miracle tip with United States patent number 2,805,671. To say nothing of Hit Parade's "40,000 filter traps"!

The smoker decided, with apparent good reason, that each filter brand was as good as the next, and he assumed, again not unreasonably, (but in fact, wrongly) that each filter brand was probably as safe as the next. He chose his filter brand as he had previously chosen his nonfilter brand—upon the basis of taste and flavor. Unfortunately, in the absence of selective filtration, the filter cigarette with the best flavor was the cigarette that filtered least. Since tar and nicotine were synonymous with flavor, the more tar and nicotine that passed by the filter, the more satisfying the taste.

The manufacturer soon discovered that any filter would suffice as a symbol of safety to the smoker, regardless of its relative efficiency, and that the only reward for high filtration was low flavor and consequently low sales. The competition that ensued was not competition in effective filtration, but competition in "juicing up" the taste by loosening the filter or utilizing more of the cheaper, stronger tobacco leaves that grow high on the plant, out of the shade.

Sales of Kent, after an initial spurt, were disappointing. By 1957, the makers of Kent had found it necessary to more than double the nicotine content and nearly to double the tar content. L&M underwent similar transformations (as did Winston, which had not been notably low in tar to begin with). By 1957, L&M's "miracle of the modern miracle tip" made way for 70 per cent more nicotine and 33 per cent more tar.

The research director of a major cigarette company told one of my associates that his laboratories had for several years kept a constant record of the tar and nicotine yields of his competitors' brands, and that the graphs charting the rise and fall in tar and nicotine content of these brands occasionally disclosed a remarkable pattern: As word would leak out that a *Reader's Digest* or *Consumer's Union* analysis of comparative tar and nicotine yields was drawing nigh, the tar and nicotine yield of many of the major brands dropped lower and lower. Then, as soon as the *Reader's Digest* or *Consumer's Union* had published its results, the tar and nicotine levels would swing sharply upward. The manufacturer had the best of all possible worlds—a high safety rating from *Reader's Digest* or *Consumer's Union* and added flavor from the reduction in the efficiency of his filter. The smoker, on the other hand, had peace of mind, a flavorsome smoke, and little protection.

The Blatnik Committee made the startling discovery that several of the best-selling filter cigarettes actually produced greater quantities of tar and nicotine than did the much maligned nonfilters. The cigarette manufacturers had thus preserved the illusion of safety while making certain that their cigarette tasted "good like a cigarette should."

The Committee's conclusions were stark and compelling:

> . . . The Federal Trade Commission has failed in its statutory duty to "prevent deceptive acts or practices" in filter-cigarette advertising.
>
> The activities of the Commission to prevent this deception were weak and tardy. As a result, the connection between filter-tip cigarettes and "protection" has become deeply embedded in the public mind.
>
> The Federal Trade Commission has failed to approach the problems of false and misleading advertising with vigor and diligence.
>
> The members of the Commission should therefore immediately critically study the organizational structure of the Commission, its procedures and its personnel, and take such action as will insure that the Commission will be able to promptly and effectively prevent deceptive practices and misleading advertising.

In effect, alternative courses were open to the Federal Trade Commission. They could have set standard efficiency tests for filtration to bring order out of the chaos of conflicting claims. Few scientists doubt that fair and meaningful standards could be established with reasonable ease and speed.

Or they could have secured the elimination of all tar and nicotine claims for filters. The virtue of this course was its perfect simplicity. Its appeal to a Commission weary of distinguishing between valid and fraudulent filter claims was irresistible. Thus, early in 1960, in the words of Lois Maddox Miller and James Monahan, writing in the *Reader's Digest*, the Commissioner "officially knocked the tar out of cigarette advertising" by obtaining the mutual consent of each of the major cigarette companies to withdraw from the tar derby—stimulated by the thinly veiled threat of Commission prosecution. The form of the consent was simplicity itself:

The undersigned states on behalf of ————————————

its intention to omit from cigarette advertising references, direct or implied, to health benefits to be derived from the use of cigarettes produced by it. It is understood this statement includes references to tar and nicotine.

As seemingly fragile as this agreement is, no company has yet dared openly to violate it.

The agreement pleased virtually no one with the exception of the Commission itself—former Chairman Kintner hailed his Commission's decision as a "landmark." And the agreement also suited that powerful segment of the cigarette industry which had always been uneasy about the filter—manufacturers who considered the very marketing of a filter an admission of the potential harm in smoke. For these manufacturers, the agreement meant that they were free to ignore the evidence against smoking. While the smoker had been relieved of the noise and confusion of competing filter claims, it was also true that filter ads no longer served as a reminder of the hazards of unfiltered smoke.

The unhappy result was that sales of nonfilter cigarettes actually stopped declining. In nonfilter ads, filters were disparaged by such innuendoes as, "Smoking more now but enjoying it less?"; "Have a *real* cigarette, have a Camel"; "Remember how good cigarettes used to taste? Luckies still do"; and "No flat, filtered-out flavor!"; while the high-filtration cigarettes, unable to advertise their relative safety, either sank from view or barely held their own.

Although the mazes of charts and graphs disappeared from the filter ads, the artful copywriter succeeded in making, implicitly, health claims which had before been explicit, with perhaps none so clever as the cigarette which "Gives you more of what you switched to a filter for." Parliament coyly promised an "extra margin." Of what? Of safety, naturally— and to make sure that no viewer missed the point, each ad featured an unmistakable safety symbol: a crash helmet, fencer's mask, life preserver, parachute, safety belt, even a stunt driver's "protective" padding.

Nonfilter cigarettes, too, began to utilize the techniques of implied safety. "Purity," "mildness," "gentleness," "freshness"—each has obvious connotations of both flavor and healthfulness. Pall Mall even suggested that it filtered without a filter as "Pall Mall's greater length travels and gentles the smoke."

One brand focused upon its asserted "coolness" as evidence of its health-giving properties, although the temperature at which smoke enters the mouth is universally considered irrelevant to the chemical composition of the smoke. Moreover, it has ben demonstrated rather conclusively that all cigarette smoke enters the mouth at or near room temperature with surprisingly little variation. Another brand boasted a "white ash," utilizing white to suggest purity and, hence, safety, though in fact the color of the ash depends upon the composition of the paper used and is again irrelevant to the problem of tar and nicotine production.

Perhaps worse, there was much less incentive for the cigarette manufacturer to commit great sums of money toward the development of more efficient or selective filters since he had little promise of being able commercially to exploit his developments.

There have been recent indications that the FTC will reconsider its 1960 decision if prodded by an endorsement of the filtration principle from the Surgeon General's Advisory Committee. Nevertheless, the Commission will remain troubled, and I think properly so, by the fear that if it sanctioned comparative filter advertisements on a basis of Commission-approved testing standards, the advertiser would be able to convey the impression that a relatively high-filtration cigarette was absolutely safe—with a government test rating to prove it. While there is, as we have seen, substantial evidence that high-filtration cigarettes are safer, we certainly have no assurance that they are *safe*. Perhaps if all cigarette ads and commercials were required to contain adequate warning of the hazards inherent in smoking, and then permitted to assert the relative safety of high-filtration cigarettes, a more desirable balance could be struck. I shall consider this possibility in more detail in the last chapter.

7

The Smokers

Parents (if not sociologists) are apt to view their adolescent offspring as members of an alien subspecies, finding little similarity between eccentric teen-age behavior patterns and their own "rational" behavior. With respect to smoking habits, at least, it is quite true that the behavior of the teen-ager in taking up smoking involves psychological, even physiological, phenomena quite distinct from the behavior of his parents in perpetuating their own smoking habit. (Whether parental smoking behavior can fairly be characterized as more rational, however, is another question.)

It is thus clear that, excepting outright prohibition, there is available no single, all-embracing panacea for the "smoking problem." The educational techniques which have proved successful in restraining the adolescent on the threshold of smoking may make little impression upon the moderate pack-a-day adult smoker, reluctant to admit that his "moderate" habit is likely to cause him severe damage. And such techniques will surely be wasted on the heavy smoker who may be acutely aware of the hazards, even to the point of chronic anxiety, but who finds himself unshakably addicted to smoking.

Educators and behavioral scientists have tended to concentrate on restricting the recruitment of adolescents to smoking while expending considerably less effort toward increasing the population of adult ex-smokers. Dr. Horn comments, "Somehow it seems to have been easier to gain both approval and funds for research on *Why Children Smoke* than for corresponding studies on adults." This preoccupation with the adolescent smoker is hardly surprising. It is plainly motivated, in part, by the natural desire to protect children. How else can be explained the behavior of the cigarette company executive who spends his days haranguing the "antibac" and his nights pleading with his children not to smoke? Besides, a campaign to dissuade children from becoming smokers poses no threat to the cherished habit of the adult smoker. Dr. George Gallup discovered in a 1957 poll that adult smokers strenuously objected to an antismoking campaign for adults but were quite willing to support such a campaign if limited to children.

There are, of course, sound reasons for placing the problem of teen-age smoking in the forefront of any smoking control program. There is evidence that the teen-age smoking population had been expanding at an accelerating rate while adult smoking has tended to level off and even decline. One survey of teen-age smoking patterns reported that in 1959, 25 per cent of children between the ages of 13 and 19 were regular smokers but that by 1961, the figure had jumped to 35 per cent, an alarming 40 per cent increase.

In the January 1963 issue of *Fortune* Magazine, there appeared a chronicle of the troubles besetting the cigarette industry. The authors could find only one source for manufacturer cheer: "There is one area at least in which the industry can apparently look forward to a substantial increase. This is among the teen-agers."

The teen-age smoking problem is thus truly of prime importance, but it is well to bear in mind that if the cigarette companies were to gain not a single new recruit among the school population but were able only to maintain their present clientele, there would be no appreciable decline in lung-cancer rates, nor in deaths from heart disease for nearly 30 years. Moreover, as we shall see, smoking among adults is probably the principal single cause of smoking among adolescents.

In 1951 the Indian psychologist R. A. Phanishayi polled a group of Indian University students, all smokers, on the factors motivating their smoking. Each student was required to select from a list of 24 items only those reasons which had motivated his initial decision to become a smoker. Among the items checked most frequently were the following:

1. I thought there was nothing wrong in doing so (52 per cent).
2. I thought there must be something attractive about it because so many people do so (48 per cent).
3. I thought that a trial would cost nothing (48 per cent).

Psychologists are naturally reluctant to assume that a subject's expressed reasons for his own behavior truly reflect his psychological motivations. Nevertheless, several subsequent studies in this country tend to support the conclusion that Phanishayi's subjects had accurately identified the factors motivating their first attempts at smoking.

Phanishayi's study was significant because it indicated that both positive and negative factors play a role in determining the adolescents' smoking behavior. His subjects tended to smoke because their view of smoking as a "normal and expected form of behavior" was coupled with the absence of concern for the health consequences of smoking.

The first job of the educator plainly is to teach the adoles-

cent that there is indeed something medically wrong in smoking—that the cost of smoking in human, as well as monetary,
terms is very great indeed.

How do you convince a teen-ager of the risks of smoking?
The exasperated parent will advise you that the only conceivable way to head off the teen-ager from smoking is to
insist that he smoke. By offering him a cigarette on every
conceivable occasion, you may be able to implant in him the
suspicion that cigarette smoking is an obligation which he
owes to his parents. Thenceforward, naturally, he will have
nothing whatsoever to do with smoking.

The Earl of Arran, however, recommended quite the oppo-
site approach:

. . . Surely the need for a major campaign against cigarette
smoking is evident and urgent. A circular and a few pamphlets will have about as much effect as a wet sponge. What
is wanted is something to impress, to jolt—and, yes—to
frighten; for example, a horror film to be shown in every
school in the country; compulsory lectures for school children, blinking no facts, omitting no details and portraying
cancer in all its grim reality. . . .

Who is right? Fortunately, we needn't speculate. Dr. Horn
and his associates from the American Cancer Society conducted a broad series of educational experiments in the
Portland High School system during the school year 1958-59
to answer the questions, "What shall we tell them?" and
"How shall we tell them?"

Dr. Horn divided the Portland schools into six experimental groups. One was treated as a control group and subjected
to no special efforts to discourage them from smoking. Each
of the five remaining groups was subjected to a program of
smoking education based upon one of five alternative approaches.

The results of these experiments were striking and, more

important, very encouraging. The first experimental group was subjected to a series of old-fashioned, heavy-handed sermons against the hazards of smoking. The children were apparently unmoved. Those who already smoked continued smoking, and others became smokers with the same frequency as the control group that had no course of instruction on smoking.

A second approach exhorted the student to inform his parents and family of the hazards of smoking (in the hope, of course, that the students' pedagogical task would be reflected in his own smoking habit). This attempt to treat the child as "father to the man" was similarly unsuccessful.

The three remaining approaches were labeled by Dr. Horn the "contemporary," the "remote," and the "both-sided." The contemporary approach dwelled upon the immediate disadvantages of smoking: the cost and unattractiveness of the habit, as well as the deleterious effect upon athletic capacity. The remote approach emphasized, in a rational, unemotional context the relationship of cigarette smoking to lung cancer. To this mixture, the both-sided approach added a touch of permissiveness, by acknowledging (without glamorizing) the pleasure and social rewards which could be derived from smoking.

Dr. Horn gave an illustration of a sample pamphlet embodying the remote approach: "You've heard a lot of arguments about smoking cigarettes. We have something new to say. We have learned many facts that lead to the conclusion that the smoking of cigarettes can cause lung cancer. We had not known this, but now there isn't much doubt. Here is some of the evidence . . . think about it before you decide to smoke."

It may come as a cold shock to parents, but Dr. Horn discovered that teen-agers are unmistakably inclined to rational thought and equally rational behavior. Although the recruitment rate among the control group boys (the percentage of the boys who took up the smoking habit during the eight months of the study) was 13 per cent, the recruitment rate among the boys who were subjected to the rational and dispassionate "remote" approach was only 7.7 per cent—a reduction of approximately 40 per cent. Moreover, the results of "both-sided" education were nearly as encouraging, yielding a recruitment rate for boys of slightly over 9 per cent.

Among the girls in the control group, the recruitment rate was 6.4 per cent. For the girls in both "remote" and "contemporary" groups, the percentage of new smokers was reduced by more than two-thirds to recruitment rates of around 2 per cent. With the girls, the "both-sided" materials produced a recruitment rate of 3.4 per cent, nearly half that of the control group.

Incidentally, the Earl of Arran is apparently wrong. Horror stories depicting the ravages of smoking have little effect on the smoking habits of children. Dr. Horn noted that there was no noticeable drop in the recruitment rate among two separate large groups of adolescents who had been subjected to highly dramatic educational material. (This substantiates my own suspicion that after television, radio, the movies and teen-age magazines, there is little chance of horrifying our teen-agers about anything!) Many students were entranced by the gory details, but it didn't affect their smoking behavior in the least.

Today, some four years after the Portland study, Dr. Horn's findings have been translated into the superb educational materials of the American Cancer Society. An energetically pursued educational program constructed upon the foundation of these materials may well be sufficient to brake the spiraling rise in teen-age smoking.

Yet education alone cannot eradicate the phenomenon of teen-age smoking. As a British educator perceptively observed in a letter to the *Manchester Guardian:* "The eventual aim must be to make smoking unfashionable for young people.

Only when to smoke cigarettes means to be 'not with it,' can we expect to see any dramatic results." Yet the teen-age smoker is today "with it" primarily because teen-age smoking is a reflection of adult smoking. So long as smoking remains fashionable among adults it will be fashionable for teen-agers to smoke.

The government of Denmark has recognized this simple truth. A major element in its secondary school smoking-education program was a letter directed to the parents of every school child citing the importance of parental persuasion and example in affecting the child's decision to smoke. The greatest good served by the letter was to convince significant numbers of parents to abandon their own smoking habit. This act of faith in the evidence against smoking—a repudiation of the fashion of smoking—undoubtedly had more effect upon the children's attitudes than a score of well-meaning parental lectures.

To paraphrase a Rockefeller, if we could only take care of the problem of adult smoking, the problem of teen-age smoking would take care of itself.

But I can scarcely recommend the education of adults to the dangers of smoking as a rewarding avocation. Although a relatively high proportion of adults is generally aware that serious charges have been leveled at the cigarette, many remain skeptical in the absence of clear-cut government action evidencing the government's own acceptance of the case against smoking. As we noted in an earlier chapter, the unrestricted flow of cigarette advertising, quite aside from its content, is viewed by the smoker as evidence that the government does not consider the threat of smoking severe enough to warrant restriction of cigarette advertising.

Phanishayi's students, as confirmed smokers, confessed that they are now dependent upon cigarettes for companionship (75 per cent), warmth (71 per cent), and as a tonic for worry and anxiety (60 per cent). Is it any wonder that the smoker will accept nothing less than 100 per cent proof before he reluctantly determines to alter this habit?

The city of Edinburgh, Scotland, invested substantial sums of money and energy in a six-months saturation campaign for the medical salvation of Edinburgh's smokers. At the close of the year, Edinburgh apparently had not succeeded in altering the smoking habits of its adult population nor even in convincing a larger segment of its population that smoking caused lung cancer.

Nevertheless, the number of smokers who do abandon their habit is surprisingly large; it grows larger as the smoker approaches the age when cancer and death are no longer remote and abstract concepts.

A Cancer Society survey of 43,000 American adults disclosed that 38 per cent of the college graduates between the gaes of 50 and 59 were ex-smokers, while among college graduates between the ages of 30 and 39, the percentage was a more modest but nonetheless significant 23 per cent. Also, you may recall that among the Massachusetts doctors, for whom the ravages of cigarette smoking are vastly more meaningful than bare statistics, the percentage of nonsmokers grew by 32 per cent in the 5-year period 1954-59.

As Dr. Horn has said:

> There is a clear cut connection between belief in smoking as a cause of lung cancer and smoking behavior. Differences range from 46 per cent accepting as against 32 per cent rejecting a causal relationship among those who smoke a pack or more a day, to the other extreme of 72 per cent accepting the relationship as against 8 per cent rejecting it among those who have given up smoking in the past 8 years.

And C. M. Fletcher noted that at a recent 2½-hour meeting in London of 200 chest physicians "only three cigarettes were seen to be smoked."

But what of the pitiable creatures who tell you that they are willing to believe all that you say of the hazards of smoking, but are nevertheless helpless in the grip of their "addiction"? Do we dismiss them as moral weaklings lacking, simply, common willpower and reluctantly abandon them to their singularly unattractive fate? Or are they in any meaningful sense addicts, incapable of helping themselves?

We are all sadly familiar with grim tales of family or friends so dependent upon cigarettes that not even the onset of lung cancer or a coronary could induce them to stop. A medical friend once told me of a colleague, an orthopedic surgeon, so wedded to his cigarettes that even when his schedule forced him to perform a series of operations without leaving the operating room, he could not bring himself to forgo his smoking break. As he would finish each operation he would retire to a far corner of the operating room where an attendant nurse could lift his mask, light his cigarette for him, and place it between his lips so that he might have the few puffs to sustain him through the next operation.

I think my most maddening encounter with tobacco addiction occurred during World War II. With my brother off in the South Pacific, Mother and I were forced to manage as best we could the family farm near Portland. For months we had hunted for an able-bodied hand among the derelicts who drifted in and out of Portland's skid row and occasionally could be tempted into a day or two of farm work. We had little success until one day we chanced upon a likable old fellow who applied himself cheerfully and soberly to the tasks at hand.

Mother and I were delighted, and the farm prospered, after a fashion, until the day the snuff ran out. At that moment he politely but firmly announced to Mother that he was off to Portland to get his "Copenhagen." Mother offered him cigarettes and even chewing tobacco (though where Mother was to get chewing tobacco, I can't quite recall). But he stood steadfast for his snuff. Not only would his pilgrimage into Portland mean the loss of the better part of a day's work, but Mother feared that once he got back to town we were not likely to see him again.

After I received a frantic S.O.S. from Mother at the school in Portland where I was then teaching, I set off through the streets of Portland, trudging wearily from one tobaccionist to another. Cigarettes were hard enough to find, but snuff, I soon discovered, was a rare commodity. Nonsmoking friends, when passing a store with cigarettes in stock, would pick up a few packs for their smoking friends—which included me at that time. So, it was usually possible to produce a pack or two of cigarettes when the need demanded, but I had no friends who stocked up on snuff. In despair, I finally prevailed upon a sympathetic storekeeper to spare me two tins of "Copenhagen."

In true Western fashion, the farm was saved.

It is hardly a connoisseur's enthusiasm which keeps the cigarette smoker coming back for more. A remarkable American Cancer Society poll disclosed that *one out of every eight regular smokers derives no pleasure whatever from his smoking.* Fifty-eight per cent said they derived some modicum of pleasure from their cigarettes, but not enough to justify the cost. A contented hard core of only 14 per cent maintained that they considered their habit pleasurable, worth the cost, and safe. "Surely," commented Dr. Horn, "there must be no other industry which has so many dissatisfied customers."

One need only examine the imaginative array of products marketed to aid the smoker in separating himself from his habit (and their apparent commercial success) to illustrate both the universality of the desire to quit and the great difficulty in achieving it. It includes cigarette cases that can be set to deliver one cigarette at 2-hour intervals (remaining locked shut during the interim) and pills to relieve the craving for nicotine (usually containing lobeline, a nicotine substitute which has been used to good effect particularly by anti-smoking clinics in Sweden).

Then there are the mountains of advice to the cigarette-lorn. Several excellent and responsible (and profitable) treatises have painstakingly outlined one method or another for breaking the cigarette habit. Equally, volumes of nonsense have been written about smoking cures in books, magazines, and newspapers. Each of these phenomena attests to the stranglehold which smoking exercises over many smokers as well as to their frustrated desire to give it up.

An experiment conducted in 1945 gave some indication of the extent to which the nicotine in cigarettes exerts a hold on the heavy smoker. The investigators enlisted a group of twenty-four heavy smokers, each of whom had conceded that he would have difficulty giving up smoking. These subjects were placed on a month-long diet of a brand of cigarettes naturally low in nicotine to which, without warning, nicotine was added or removed. By altering the nicotine content it was possible to observe the effect of nicotine deprivation.

When unknowingly switched from high-nicotine to low-nicotine cigarettes, twelve of the twenty-four evidenced distinct symptoms of withdrawal: increased irritability, diminished ability to concentrate, and a vague sense of "inner hunger." (What is "outer hunger" by the way?) Of this group of twelve, three eventually became adjusted to the low-nicotine cigarettes, but the remaining nine were unreconciled to the lack of nicotine throughout the month of the experiment. The other twelve experienced an initial undefined lack of satisfaction when shifted from high-nicotine to low-nicotine cigarettes but quickly became used to the change. Curiously, all twenty-four were grateful for no-nicotine cigarettes when no cigarettes at all was the alternative.

This and subsequent studies support the general belief that the smoking habit is part physiological and part psychological addiction. Whether this amounts to "true addiction" or not is an argument best left to semanticists. The fact remains that many people who are otherwise capable of exerting a normal quantum of willpower simply cannot stop smoking. Until a better description of the addictive nature of smoking comes along. I shall be content with Lord Salter's conception of cigarette smoking as a "vice" rather than a "luxury":

> Nonsmokers have often said to me: "Why don't people make a strong effort of will and end this bad habit? In a short time the urge would go." I always thought they were wrong, but I had no conclusive answer until the experience of the last war, when we had a human experiment of a very rare kind and on a very large scale. Millions on the Continent of Europe were forcibly prevented from smoking at all for some years, and it might have been expected that by the end of that time the urge would have gone. Yet when cigarettes became available, but in scanty supply, there was hardly any other commodity which was so eagerly sought after. You could buy almost anything with a packet of cigarettes. I say that, not to suggest that many people cannot and should not abandon smoking, but to show that it is not as easy as may have been suggested by the noble Lord, Lord Fisher of Lambeth, and the noble Viscount Lord Samuel.
>
> I should like to add that I think cigarette smoking—and I speak as one who has been an addict at times in my life—partakes of the nature of a vice, as distinct from a luxury, in the sense that most people smoke cigarettes at least as much to avoid the discomfort of not smoking them as for the positive pleasure they get. I myself find that, when I want to take a cigarette, that is what is mainly in my mind. I do not get much positive pleasure, but it is uncomfortable not to smoke one. On the other hand, when I smoke a cigar it is not because I have had a strong urge to do it; it is because I get positive pleasure. Now, it is very much easier to forgo a luxury than to cut clear of a vice, and, in this sense at least, I think that cigarette smoking is a vice.
>
> I remember during a period of economic depression being in Paris and going to buy a packet of cigarettes from an old

"So that's agreed then, we'll drop the sex angle and play up the death wish."

*"Figures prove that **fewer** people are giving up smoking Park Royale than any other brand."*

"For a man who was going to quit smoking today,
you aren't exactly starting off with a bang."

"I can't afford both so I've decided on cirrhosis."

woman in a kiosk. I remarked: "Well, madam, I hope you
are not suffering too much from these bad times," to which,
in that epigrammatic wit which you often find in all classes
of our French neighbours, she replied at once: "No, Sir, I
am not doing so badly. You see, I have the good fortune to
have my business based upon one of the principal vices of
man, and there could be no surer foundation." I think there
is some truth in her remark.

The significance of the addictive character of smoking cannot be overstated. To the extent that smoking is addictive,
the argument that the adult who continues smoking in the
face of the medical evidence is merely exercising his freedom
of choice is unsound. Moreover, the addictive quality of
smoking makes it all the more urgent and imperative that
every reasonable resource be directed at intercepting the
nonsmoking teen-ager before he initiates a "trial" of smoking.

Lastly, the shadow of addiction bars us from dismissing
the unregenerate smoker as unworthy of help. He is not a
willful suicide. And if he cannot be helped to abandon smoking, then we must do what we can to take the sting out of his
addiction by making cigarettes as safe as possible.

8

Redressing
the Balance

Carrie Nation would surely have regarded me as a pale recruit for her ax-wielding, Antisaloon League squads. I have on several occasions taken pains to express my belief that prohibition is not an acceptable solution to the smoking problem. Imagine my surprise at the curiously savage editorial which appeared in the *Portland Oregonian:*

Big Brother Knows Best

In asking that the federal government require that cigarette advertisements contain a statement that "smoking is a health hazard," Senator Maurine Neuberger is following the lead of Great Britain, where, in an unprecedented campaign, the government has plastered the billboards with advertisements designed to discourage cigarette smoking.

It is a new twist to the philosophy of prohibition. Big Brother doesn't outlaw supposedly harmful habits, as did America through the hapless 18th Amendment; he just takes the stump to promote his view of the right and healthful.

Whatever view one may hold of smoking or the advertisements promoting it, the measures advocated by Senator Neuberger have truly appalling implications. Automobiles,

115

too, can be fatal. Must one, therefore, be required to stress
that fact in offering them for sale? What about selling
aspirin in quantities sufficient for a fatal dosage? And
will refrigerators and other appliances be sold only with the
published admonition that the buyer must not close the door
from the inside?

It would be possible, perhaps, for the government to provide a
book of fatherly advice with every product to instruct against
its misuse by damned fools without minds of their own. But
we hope we do not live to see the day. The buyer who does
not yet know of the possible causal chain between cigarettes
and cancer, or of the probable effect of driving a car into a
pedestrian or swallowing a bottle of aspirin or bleaching
fluid is not worth the saving at the risk of deadening, in all
the rest of us, the responsibility of choice.

I had always believed that educating a consumer to the
proved dangers of a product, then leaving to him the choice
of consuming it or not, was the very antithesis of prohibition.
I half-suspect that the editor was disappointed that I had not
advocated prohibition. Perhaps, on the tip of his pen, was an
antiprohibition sermon he was itching to deliver; temptation
may have so overwhelmed him that he chose to disregard
what I had said and to label me a prohibitionist anyway.

But aside from the relatively trivial problem of mislabeling
me, the editorial does raise serious questions. Why, indeed,
should cigarette commercials be treated differently from automobile, aspirin, or refrigerator commercials? (It is a grim
coincidence that the death tolls from lung cancer and from
auto accidents are roughly equivalent.)

An elaborate dialectic upon the relative social utility of the
automobile, the aspirin, the refrigerator, and the cigarette
would not, I am afraid, be particularly enlightening (I am not
prepared to argue with the smoker who swears that his need
for a cigarette at any given moment far surpasses his need
for mechanical transportation, a cold beer, or even relief from

a headache). But I do think it worth noting that all but the cigarette in some definable measure contribute to our standards of living or health.

Moreover, neither the automobile, the refrigerator, nor the aspirin presents a hazard if used in the manner in which it is normally intended to be used. But the one-half to one-pack-a-day smoker—the moderate smoker—does subject himself to considerable hazard though he utilizes cigarettes in precisely the manner envisioned by the cigarette commercials.

Of course, there are reasonably well-advertised automobile speed limits, there are carefully prescribed dosages on aspirin bottles, and there have been recent safety campaigns (aided, not sabotaged by the industry) warning of the hazards of unattended refrigerators. Besides, when an automobile strikes down a pedestrian, the auto's causal role in the death of the pedestrian is readily apparent. Not so the internal and subtle role of the cigarette in disease. Have you ever seen a newspaper account of a traffic accident conclude with some such statement from the Automobile Manufacturers' Association as these? "The association between the impact of automobiles and death is merely statistical," or "Science has shown that certain individuals inherit both the tendency to be struck by autos and the tendency simultaneously to expire."

The *Oregonian* sentences the ignorant to a somber fate: "The buyer who does not yet know of the possible causal chain between cigarettes and cancer . . . is not worth the saving. . . ." Why? Have the *Oregonian* and its fellow news purveyors been so punctilious in reporting the medical community's verdict against smoking that no careful reader could fail to perceive the precise proven relationship of smoking to disease? And, is the 12- or 13-year-old who cannot differentiate between the consensus of the scientific community and the paid pronouncements of a tobacco industry publicity organ guilty of mortal sin?

The American Cancer Society's poll established that only 16 per cent of the general population were completely convinced that cigarette smoking is a "major cause of lung cancer." *

But we do not need polls to measure the extent of public misinformation. Take the editor of the *Oregonian*, for example. He writes of the "possible" relationship between smoking and disease. "Possible" is hardly an accurate description of the conclusiveness of the evidence. A week or so earlier the *Oregonian* had ridiculed the use of the word "epidemic" to describe the rising death toll of cancer among smokers. Yet, there is a consensus among public health officials that the spiraling death rate from lung cancer is precisely epidemic in character. The editor also stated that the Public Health Service "has yet to make a flat statement that cigarettes cause lung cancer." Yet, the Public Health Service has said, "The weight of evidence at present shows that smoking—particularly cigarette smoking—is a principal reason for the rising death rate from lung cancer in the past 30 years." Finally, the editor dismisses smoking, along with alcohol, as one of the "popular vices," suggesting that, at least as far as he can see, the essence of the furor about smoking is moral, not medical.

That he is thus misinformed and confused, and that 84 per cent of his fellow Americans are similarly misinformed and confused, is a tribute to the success of the tobacco industry in suppressing, distorting, and overcoming by psychological manipulation the truth about smoking. I doubt that it is a

---

* It is quite true that a far larger percentage sense that smoking is to some ill-defined extent associated with disease. This latent association came to the surface before a national television audience one day last summer, as a contestant on the television program, "Password," when prodded by his partner for the word most readily brought to mind by "cigarette," answered abruptly, "cancer." The audience was delighted. I feel confident their delight was shared neither by the master of ceremonies, the network, nor the advertising fraternity.

tribute from which anyone could derive much inner satisfaction, but I believe that the event should not pass into
history without public notice.

But now that I have huffed and puffed at tobacco's house
for many pages and had my say of industry vice and government vacuity, I can hardly in good conscience close without
offering a constructive word or two. Since I'm not a doctor
I can't justify this book as an authoritative treatise on the
medical aspects of smoking (which it most assuredly is not),
nor can I claim any special insight into the economic, socio-
logical, psychological, or even historical aspects of the smoking
phenomenon. But I *am* a legislator, and I do make a modest
claim to be at home with questions of government responsibility. And, since this book culminates a year-long period of
relatively intense study and contemplation of the smoking
problem, I hope that my conclusions would be of some use
to those who are now called upon to chart the course of national policy with respect to smoking; namely, the Surgeon
General's Committee on Smoking.

Wherever possible, solutions must be sought within the
framework of existing legislation, though a fully adequate
program is impossible without Congressional action. As som-
nolent as the administrative agencies have thus far been, the
likelihood of prodding them to constructive action is far
greater than the possibility of arousing Congress. There is
hope that the Surgeon General's Committee will issue a
strong and unequivocal report. Should this prove true, it will
provide an immediate impetus to action. The administration
may be capable of responding quickly and energetically to
such stimulus. Congress, short of some unmentionable national calamity, is not.

I consider that there are four general sectors of government
activity in which remedial action is presently both justified
and tardy: (1) education of both the presmoking adolescent
and the adult smoker, (2) expanded research into the tech-

nology of safer smoking, (3) reform of cigarette advertising and promotion, and (4) cautionary and informative labeling of cigarette packages.

For the benefit of that fortunately small segment of our population that insists that the only justification for government action in any sphere is keeping up with the Russians, let us note dutifully that though we are told there may no longer exist a "missile gap," there most assuredly exists a "smoking education gap."

The Russian government's concern with "do-it-yourself air pollution" was described by the Soviet Deputy Health Administrator, N. F. Izmerov, during a recent visit to the United States.

"Lately in the world," Izmerov told reporters, "you can find all sorts of publications which indicate lung cancer increases with smoking." He explained that the Ministry of Health has launched a vigorous smoking education campaign employing not only conventional teaching materials but television ads, and posters as well. "Big posters," Izmerov told reporters, "telling you so many cigarettes can kill a horse— hundreds of cigarettes, I think. I don't smoke so I don't remember exactly."

The Soviet Ministry of State Education sponsored the making of a film entitled, *The Cigarette Is To Blame*. This dramatic work closes with a scene depicting its own premiere. As all of the film-makers gather to congratulate one another, one of the actors presents his cigarette case to the studio director, as if to offer him a smoke. The cigarette case pops open to reveal—a piece of candy. The humor is elemental, but the message is clear.

Nor have responsible Russian officials been loath to take a public stand on smoking. The Minister of Health described smoking as "a dangerous form of chronic poisoning of the organism which may cause serious illnesses." And, to a group of journalists puffing away on their cigarettes during an interview, Marshal Voroshilov, President of the Soviet Union, observed, "Gentlemen, smoking is a very bad habit. I regret to inform you that you are shortening your life." (I await the Tobacco Institute's dictum that communist opposition to smoking *proves* its value to capitalism.)

The Russians, of course, begin their educational campaigns with a decided advantage over the Western nations; they need not overcome the cumulative effects of multimillion-dollar cigarette advertising before they can even begin to have a net positive effect on smoking attitudes and habits.

Nevertheless, we in America do possess certain appreciable assets: the dynamic educational resources of the voluntary health associations led by the American Cancer Society, the awakening medical societies, and the maturing smoking education programs of several states and cities.

The existence of these assets suggests that a primary federal role is to coordinate, expedite, and, if necessary, finance the efforts of the voluntary associations, societies, states, and municipalities. There is no good reason why the students of Chicago, for example, should not have the benefit of smoking education techniques developed by the Jacksonville, Florida, schools. Nor should the Cancer Society fail, for lack of funds, or of public endorsement, to reach the students of every secondary school with its educational materials.

There is much that the government can do, or cause to be done, to supplement the educational materials originated by the Cancer Society and the various states. Just as Dr. Horn and his associates developed psychologically sound educational materials for children, so must there be educational programs tailored to the peculiar needs of the adult smoker. The report of the Royal College lamented the lack of "imagination" which characterizes present attempts to draw "the attention of the public to the hazards of smoking." The activities of the cancer specialists at the Roswell Park Memorial Hospital in Buffalo, New York, a State hospital, provide a glimpse of the broad spectrum of materials that can be developed to bring home to the adult the truth about smoking.

I was fascinated by the Roswell Park doctors' utilization of matchbook covers to sell their message. What more efficient advertising vehicle to reach smokers can be imagined than the back of a matchbook bearing the slogan "Smoke the money —it's healthier," or the companion matchbook emphasizing the importance of smoking a smaller portion of each cigarette with the slogan, "Measure Your Smoke For Safety. . . . Smoke Less. . . ." In an accompanying illustration the butt end of a cigarette is colored red and labeled "Danger." (The next step is to provide perpetually soggy matches—impossible to light.)

Roswell Park has also banished vending machines from the hospital confines and is now distributing quantities of an adhesive-backed, iridescent red label suitable for plastering on cigarette packages and vending machines. It bears the message "WARNING! Excessive use is dangerous to health."

Imagination was also displayed by the Cancer Society's use of recorded telephone messages describing the risks of smoking. This method was extraordinarily successful in Washington and attracted thousands of curious callers who received a mild but thoroughly convincing oral essay on the ravages of smoking.

Surely these imaginative efforts can be profitably exploited on a national scale by efficient government programming and aid.

I see no reason, moreover, why the advertisers should not be met at their own doorsteps by a campaign of government-sponsored TV, radio, magazine, and newspaper advertisements, all with the verve of Madison Avenue, to depict the dangers of smoking. A correspondent in the English Medical Journal *Lancet* had the idea:

Can no one in Saville Row, of all places, plagiarize the idyllic scene of clean and manly young man with damsel pure and beautiful, apple blossom overhead: "Darling you smell so nice, I'm so glad you gave up smoking." Or, leaning against his expensive car: "I could never have fallen for a girl who smoked." Can't they pay a fee to a racing motorist, a handsome actor, or even a pop singer, whose photograph would say with a smile: "I never smoke *now*."

It is also to be hoped that the now discordant and conflicting voices of government officials will eventually be replaced by statements such as that of the British Health Minister, Enoch Powell, who told his countrymen that they displayed an astonishing lack of intellect if they continued to smoke despite the evidence. Said Mr. Powell: "The same public which scans the figures of deaths on traffic accidents with close anxiety and urges rightly that nothing be left untried that could reduce the annual total of about 7,000 road deaths, looks with apparent unconcern at the figure of deaths from lung cancer—already nearly four times as large at over 25,000 and rising year by year. All but a tiny fraction of those deaths would not have occurred but for smoking."

I recommend the creation within the Department of Health, Education and Welfare of a separate and distinct Division of Smoking Control charged with the authority to aid states and private associations in the development and dissemination of smoking education materials, and supplied with the funds and authority to conduct a broad range of educational activities on a national scale. Such activities should include the use of posters in federal buildings and on federal vehicles, and the purchase of time and space from commercial advertising media for advertisements calculated to discourage smoking. This can be done by executive order, though it would be strengthened by a legislative mandate.

The standard response of the cigarette company executive

when pressed for comment on the relationship between smoking and health is that the real need now is for "further research." I agree. But I suspect there is this difference in our concepts of needed research: The industry claims that more research is needed to determine *if* smoking plays a causal role in disease; I want more research because we *know* that it does.

Though we have known of smoking's causal role for a relatively long time, we have much to learn of its mechanism. For example, though we have isolated various carcinogens in tobacco tar they are not considered sufficiently potent alone to account for the high incidence of lung cancer in smokers. The interaction of these carcinogens with suspected co-carcinogens in the smoke remains a relative mystery.

With respect to the immediate pragmatic issues of smoking control, we lack sufficient knowledge of the "where-do-we-go-from-here" variety. We need to isolate, identify, and effect the removal of the incriminated agents in smoke. To this end we must press for the development of more efficient filters, chemical additives for filters, and the development of low-nicotine, low-tar-producing strains of tobacco.

There is work, too, for the behavioral scientist. We do not yet know the precise nature of tobacco addiction, nor do we understand why some smokers are able to relinquish smoking and stay "unhooked" the very first time, while others quit "a thousand times."

We need to stimulate research by the tobacco industry itself—that is, meaningful research, not projects designed primarily to discredit, if possible, the results of earlier studies antagonistic to the interests of the industry. We need to step up the pace and broaden the scope of smoking-control research by National Institutes of Health, and nongovernmental institutions on grants from the Public Health Service.

Children are entitled to a full measure of our educational capacity; smoking addicts are no less entitled to any effort which might cure their habit.

Cigarette advertising, as we have seen earlier, is a twin-edged sword; both blades need badly to be blunted. On the one hand, there is the unabashed resort to psychological manipulation, including the youth-oriented cast of a major segment of the advertising matter. On the other hand, quite aside from content, there is the repeated publication of the ads, tending to convince the smoker that the government does not consider the threat of smoking sufficiently severe to warrant restriction of cigarette advertising.

Advertising thus serves both to amplify the lure of smoking for the nonsmoker and to reassure the smoker. Nevertheless, one can hardly approach the task of regulating advertising content with any degree of enthusiasm. As a liberal, I find myself troubled by the suggestion that the government dictate to a broadcaster or publisher what he can say and what he cannot say about anything, including cigarettes. We have accepted in our regulatory legislation the premise that what an advertiser says must not be deceptive but we have been properly reluctant to go beyond the elimination of deception.

If a particular cigarette company pays a baseball star $1,000 a month to smoke its Brand X and to testify to the kiddies that he smokes Brand X, the advertiser claims that there is no deception involved in the advertisement. Yet, the implied "message of the ad" (and the justification to the cigarette stockholders for paying an athlete $1,000 a month just to smoke Brand X) is that the path to the baseball Hall of Fame is strewn with Brand X butts. This message, I submit, is palpably untrue, and the advertisement is, indeed, deceptive. Similarly, advertisements plainly calculated to suggest that there is a cause-and-effect relationship between smoking and social and romantic success are equally deceptive.

The degree of deception is, of course, relative. The deceptive qualities which I have described inhere to some degree in all advertising. The distinction, I submit, is that tolerances for deception in cigarette advertising must be narrower than for products whose use involves only the risk of loss of the purchase price, not life.

For these reasons, I recommend that the Federal Trade Commission utilize its substantive rule-making powers to adopt the cigarette-advertising guidelines established by the British Independent Television Authority. Through these guides, advertisers are enjoined to avoid all advertisements which fall within the following five classes of objectionable matter:

1. Advertisements that greatly overemphasize the pleasure to be obtained from cigarettes. 2. Advertisements featuring the conventional heroes of the young. 3. Advertisements appealing to pride or general manliness. 4. Advertisements using a fashionable social setting to support the impression that cigarette smoking is a 'go-ahead' habit or an essential part of the pleasure and excitement of modern living. 5. Advertisements that strikingly present romantic situations and young people in love, in such a way as to seem to link the pleasures of such situations with the pleasures of smoking.*

I can think of no government action relating to the smoking problem which would be more universally acclaimed than this surgery of the malignancies of cigarette advertising. I might add that these guidelines are not necessarily fated to invoke the eternal wrath of the advertisers. "It may be better," one British advertiser was quoted as saying, "to have some restrictions to work within rather than to have people

* On July 9, 1963, the Tobacco Institute suggested, somewhat timidly, that since "smoking is a custom for adults" the members henceforth utilize "good judgment and good taste" in avoiding advertisements tending "to promote or encourage smoking among youth." The revolutionary impact of this suggestion upon the content of cigarette ads can be judged by the reaction of Joseph F. Cullman, III, President of Philip Morris, Inc., who commented that the Institute's suggestion was in line with existing company policy. In other words, "no change."

sniping at you all the time and not to know whether you are right or wrong."

The FTC is seasoned in the use and enforcement of guidelines. Of course, the implementation of guidelines requires constant policing. We know from dismal experience that past guides have fallen rather easy prey to the fertile inventiveness of Madison Avenue in devising ads that achieve technical compliance while violating the spirit of the guidelines.

The guidelines would be helpful, but not sufficient. Even a cigarette ad which fully complied with the ITV guides would not afford the viewer, in the words of the Royal College, "evidence of active concern by the government." That effect can only be achieved by a requirement that every cigarette commercial and advertisement contain adequate affirmative warning of the hazards of smoking.

The FTC has recognized that it possesses power to compel such warnings. If the Surgeon General's Committee confirms the indictment of smoking, the responsibility will then rest with the FTC to utilize that power.

A universal requirement that cigarette ads and commercials contain adequate warning will, I think, also serve to pave the way for a solution to what is currently the FTC's insoluble dilemma. The FTC now prohibits health claims for high filtration cigarettes low in tar, nicotine, or phenol, on the grounds that any such claims would have the effect of suggesting to the public that the high-filtration cigarette was not only a safer smoke but also an absolutely safe one. However, should all cigarette advertisements, including those for filters, contain warning of the potential hazard of smoking, the danger of any viewer assuming that the filter cigarette was absolutely safe would all but vanish. With this objection removed, the very real benefits to be derived from commercial competition in effective filtration could be stimulated by an FTC-sanctioned revival of a closely supervised "Tar Derby." Once we return to a situation of open competition for the "most nearly safe" cigarette, there will naturally be a greater stimulus to industry research in filter technology.

The precise wording of the warning must be prescribed by the Commission, and it is essential that the relative space or the length of time and relative prominence to be accorded the warning must also be delineated so that the words of warning not be drowned in a sea of advertising matter.

Should the FTC fail to act or should FTC action be nullified by the courts, I think it would then be worthwhile to pursue the argument that a radio or television station which continues to carry today's cigarette advertising in the face of a clearly expressed governmental position that cigarette smoking is hazardous thereby fails to live up to the Federal Communications Act requirement that a station serve the "public interest." The FCC may then be able to step in where the FTC had unsuccessfully trod.

During the Blatnik hearings, Dr. Clarence Cook Little of the Tobacco Industry Research Committee was asked to comment upon the filter-tip phenomenon. Dr. Little, somewhat cavalierly, answered that to him filters were a matter of "complete and unenthusiastic indifference."

I must say that this was an instance in which I was at first tempted to agree with Dr. Little. After all, even if we were to spend millions of dollars and consume thousands of scarce scientific man-hours to develop the most nearly perfect filter, it would still be safer not to smoke.

To the teen-ager who is hovering between the decision to smoke or not, the promise of filters can furnish little incentive to begin a habit which has no proven virtues, but multifarious defects.

Yet there are roughly 70 million smokers in this country— the vast majority of whom have shown little inclination to abandon their habit. I fear even the most massive and efficient educational program will fail to sever the majority of confirmed smokers from their habit.

Among my office staff there were five regular cigarette smokers. As this office has become a focal point for scientists and ordinary citizens concerned about smoking, my staff has been subjected to all manner of letters, scientific papers, and diatribes about the hazards of smoking. They have typed my speeches about smoking. They have proofread articles about smoking. Several have read (voluntarily) the early chapters of this book. There were, I repeat, five smokers. There remain four today (the fifth, a male, has switched to the pipe, an expedient unfortunately of limited appeal to women).

If there is any value in filters, if we have developed or if it is possible to develop effective filters which will save even a small fraction of those now fated to succumb to smoking's diseases, then the filter cannot remain a "matter of complete and enthusiastic indifference."

There are two categories of information to which every smoker and potential smoker is entitled. First, until such time as the filter or its successor devices have proved absolutely safe, he should know that all cigarette smoking is potentially hazardous. Second, he should know at what point in the scale of relative safety stands the particular cigarette which he proposes to buy.

I am convinced that the Food and Drug Commissioner presently possesses the power under the Hazardous Substances Labeling Act to require each and every package of cigarettes to bear such information on its label.

In my opinion, the Commissioner can and should require each cigarette package sold to bear the word WARNING or CAUTION and, in the words of the Act, "an affirmative statement of the principal hazard or hazards." Moreover, the Commissioner, with the aid of the Bureau of Standards and the Public Health Service, should develop standard methods for testing the relative efficiency of filters and for measuring yields of nicotine and tar and such specific substances as phenols, which may yet be identified as the incriminated agents in the tar. He should require that such information be prominently displayed on each cigarette package in terms which are reasonably designed to be meaningful to the average smoker. The FDA should also consider requiring that a circular band be printed on each cigarette wrapper as an indicator to the smoker of the prudent length to leave a cigarette butt.

Provision must also be made for high-level, interdepartmental coordination of all smoking-control activities. Close perusal reveals that scarcely any department or regulatory agency lacks a significant role to play in any coherent smoking-control program. The Department of Health, Education and Welfare, the Departments of Commerce and Agriculture, the FTC, and the FCC are the obvious ones. But look at the Defense Department—one hardly thinks of defense as being intimately connected with the cigarette industry or smoking-connected diseases, yet the military establishment is very deeply involved in the smoking problem.

At one level the Armed Services are great customers of the cigarette companies as well as the beneficiaries of cigarette company largess (with the notable exception, as we have seen, of the Air Force). On another level the services are unconsciously instrumental in promoting smoking within the service ranks. The 5-minute smoking break is a hallowed military tradition. (You can't carry a pipe, cigars are brittle, and you can chew your nails only so long—so you smoke a cigarette.) The C-ration still yields its miniature pack, and cigarettes remain widely available to servicemen at 10 cents or less per package.

There has been, in connection with the formation of the Surgeon General's Advisory Committee, a generally informal growth of liaison channels between the various interested departments. I would like to see these channels developed, expanded, and made permanent.

The proposals I have thus far made are both moderate and feasible. But what would you really do, someone will surely ask, if you could have your way with Congress? (As if anybody after George Washington ever had!) What would the model Neuberger Smoking Control Act look like?

Of course, I would include in any legislation a directive to the Administration to perform precisely those tasks that I already have urged upon it: education, labeling, controlling of advertising, and research.

In order to promote the educational and advertising activities of the smoking-control division (particularly its program of commercial advertising and a grant-in-aid program to state education departments) and to finance federal research into the causes of cancer and the development of safer cigarettes, I would like to see an appropriate increase in the federal cigarette tax, the proceeds to be specifically earmarked for such purposes. (Iceland, incidentally, last year modified its tax structure in precisely this manner, adding a one-half cent per package increment to its cigarette tax with the proceeds earmarked for the Icelandic Cancer Society, which plans to launch a campaign to tell Icelanders of the hazards of smoking.)

In addition, the cigarette tax structure should be altered so that the tax would be levied according to the weight of the tobacco in the cigarette rather than the length, as is now the case. This change would encourage the production of cigarettes with reduced tobacco contents and correspondingly smaller tar and nicotine yields.

Moreover, cigarette tax reform can be coupled with a program of mandatory maximum controls on permissible tar, nicotine, and phenol yields of cigarettes. I would propose that no cigarette could be marketed in the United States if it yielded greater proportions of the substances than the Secretary of Health, Education and Welfare, after appropriate hearing and review, determined to be both reasonably free of hazard and technically workable. These limits could not practicably be set by Congress but would necessarily be altered from time to time to reflect advances both in medical research and in the technology of cigarette manufacture.

What of the argument that there can be no meaningful control of teen-age smoking short of a federal ban on cigarette sales to minors and on all cigarette sales from unattended vending machines.

Forty-seven states—including North Carolina and Virginia —already prohibit, by statute, the sales of cigarettes to children. These laws are, without exception, unenforced and unenforceable. Even where the authorities are willing to make a stab at enforcement, the ubiquitous unattended vending machine renders enforcement a physical impossibility.

Lawyers and sociologists class teen-age antismoking laws— together with antifornication laws—as classic examples of the futility of efforts to thwart prevailing behavior patterns by legislation. The failure of these statutes can be traced to community acceptance of teen-age smoking as normal, not antisocial, behavior. And until such time as these prevailing social attitudes toward teen-age smoking are materially altered, a federal teen-age antismoking and antivending machine law would be at best a futile gesture and at worst an administrative monstrosity. These objections would not apply, however, to a federal ban on the distribution of free cigarettes to minors. (The Treasury already prohibits a cigarette company from giving more than one free pack a day to any employee.) Nor would they apply to local antivending machine ordinances where the community social climate is conducive to meaningful enforcement.

I would add one further provision. There is probably no single spectre which so haunts the cigarette companies as the imminence of a flood of successful lawsuits by lung-cancer victims, bringing jury awards rocketing into the millions and even tens of millions of dollars. While I am not likely to be accused of being "soft on" cigarette companies, I do think it entirely appropriate that a tobacco company which faithfully complies with any national smoking-control program should be subject only to limited liability for smoking-connected diseases and that an express limit of liability should be made part of any omnibus smoking-control program.

"If tobacco were spinach," Dr. Shimkin once said, "it would have been outlawed years ago and no one would give a hoot."

But tobacco isn't spinach, and an $8,000,000,000 industry and 70 million smokers do "give a hoot." The measures which I have recommended, even if fully implemented, would not destroy the cigarette industry. Neither would they eliminate all smoking-connected diseases. They should serve to dampen the growth of cigarette sales and perhaps to cause even a moderate tapering off in absolute sales as properly informed adolescents determine not to adopt a habit which has no rational appeal to them and strong-willed adults exorcise their own addiction. Others, I know, will continue smoking. Still others will become smokers. Hopefully, the cigarettes that they consume will yield a continually diminishing hazard.

The Royal College of Physicians, in concluding its survey of the medical and social facts regarding smoking, declined to endorse cigarette prohibition. "But," warned the Royal College, "the amount of ill health and shortening of life that is attributable to smoking is now so great that means must be sought to reduce the vast and increasing prevalence of the habit. At present, both social custom and commercial pressure outbid the voice of caution and the balance must be redressed."

Appendix

For readers who desire to pursue in depth the scientists' case against smoking, there is a vast library of works from which to choose, ranging in style and complexity from the popular to the scientifically sober. The Report of the Royal College of Physicians ("*Smoking and Health:* The Royal College of Physicians of London Report on Smoking in Relation to Cancer of the Lung and Other Diseases." Pitman Medical Publishing Co. Ltd. London, 1962) is a truly superb document—admirably brief, clear, readable and exhaustive. It does not sacrifice scientific precision for the sake of its general audience. The recent publication from Consumers Union (*Smoking and the Public Interest.* Consumers Union of U.S. Inc., Mount Vernon, New York, 1963) integrates the findings of the very latest investigations and is also to be commended for its completeness.

For those whose appetite for scientific detail remains unquenched, I would recommend the series of technical papers presented at a two-day symposium sponsored jointly by the New York Academy of Medicine and the New York State Academy of Preventive Medicine reviewing the entire question of tobacco and health (James and Rosenthal, *Tobacco and Health.* Charles C.

Thomas, Springfield, Illinois, 1962) and a work which incorporates significant material relating to the psycho-social aspects of smoking (Proosdij, D. van, *Smoking: Its Influence on the Individual and Its Role in Social Medicine*. Elsevier Publishing Co., Amsterdam, 1960).

Finally, for any who are consumed with the urge to learn everything there is to know about smoking and health, there is the formidable, if slightly outdated, review of all the medical literature on tobacco published before 1961 (Larson, P. S., Haag, H. B., Silvette, H., *Tobacco—Experimental and Clinical Studies: A Comprehensive Account of the World Literature*. Ballière, Tindall & Cox, London, 1961).

Index